SMOKE WITHOUT FIRE

David Roy

HOBART BOOKS

SMOKE WITHOUT FIRE

ISBN 978-1-914322-00-6

First Published in 2021
by
Hobart Books, Oxfordshire, England
hobartbooks.com

Printed and bound in Great Britain by Biddles Ltd

PART ONE

Chapter One

Inauspicious beginnings

I had a routine of sorts – a miserable routine – in which my day started badly, tailed off dramatically and then picked up again shortly before I went to sleep for the night. At times I was either in the process of actively hating my job, or dreading the next day, or asleep; three states of being and no others. Things had always been bad there but now it was worse than ever, and deteriorating steadily. It had become almost intolerable. Whatever it was that had made me a good teacher – not a gift exactly, but a knack certainly – had gone, had left without warning like an exorcised ghost. What was left was the ineffectual shell of a teacher. I was barely a presence in my own classroom.

I realised that I couldn't change the situation, that to try was like climbing a mountain of lunacy, armed only with common sense. To try to explain that it was actually the school that was failing so dramatically was to invite scrutiny of one's teaching

1

designed to undermine and discredit, but which could always be explained away as 'supportive'. There were, you see, no bad pupils, only bad teaching, the former (had they existed) stemming exclusively from the latter.

I am sure that a lot of my colleagues realised that much of the 'bad teaching' that occurred was actually the result of deplorable pupil behaviour i.e., the pupils simply did not let the teacher teach.... but no one dared say it. Even I, a rather forthright person shall we say, was loath to make the obvious claim, certainly to anyone in authority. As a staff we had been conditioned, ground down by the unassailable reverse logic of the school's management. Even when a teacher reported an assault or some other form of terrible behaviour, they knew *they* were likely to be questioned as to what *they* had done that provoked the errant pupil to behave in such a way. It was monstrous, insane, but sadly it became the norm. I believe it's called taking a 'child-centric' approach, but phrases such as this readily transited my brain ending up in a virtual bin, labelled 'bovine faeces.'

So, if I couldn't change things what was I to do? Leave, obviously. I had tried to do so on a number of previous occasions but had never been given an interview at another school and as time went on it became more difficult. With experience came better pay and it was probably this factor more than any other which prevented a move; a headteacher was often unwilling to pay extra for that experience, preferring to take on a cheaper alternative in the form of an NQT, a newly qualified teacher.

The only way around this problem was to seek a promotion, something that I wasn't too interested in, especially not with a young family. Plenty of people did that – took a promotion – simply to move on but it did mean that the school sometimes ended up with a head of department or a head of year who was less than totally committed to their new role. Besides, I didn't trust myself to have the initiative, leadership or ambition to be a success as a manager. I didn't want the buck to stop with me and the increase in pay was relatively modest in any case.

My wife, who was also a teacher, had often urged me to leave, as had a number of colleagues, but it had got to the point where I just threw my lot in with the school. *Horses for courses.* I was the sort of teacher who could survive, if not prosper, at a school like Collegiate. The staff fell into two broad categories: those who took on the job and then, realising what a hellhole they were in, left at the first opportunity; and those who took a fatalistic approach and stayed. My view was that it was the devil I knew. I could control the children in my care and I knew the ropes. There was nothing complacent about my approach but I could manage.... except recently I couldn't. Those tricks of the trade that had stood me in such good stead for a number of years had been rendered obsolete almost overnight. I couldn't understand why, nor could I think of a suitable alternative approach to take.

My teaching style was based upon having good discipline first and foremost. Without that I was lost. It was almost as if discipline had become an ugly word with connotations of cruelty and deprival of human rights and yet discipline was what the school needed most.

The drive to work was one of the highlights of my day but it would have been better had I not had to leave the safety of my car and make the wind-lashed walk from the car park to the confines of the school. I had done it for ten years with more or less the same routine, but familiarity with what lay ahead didn't necessarily make things any easier for me. I usually dreaded work. Even listening to Black Sabbath CDs in the car didn't lift my mood. The chances of me getting through a day without confrontation and disappointment, despair and disillusion, were remote. My first two years had been the worst though. I started at Collegiate High School in 1998 as a newly qualified teacher. I was relatively young at thirty-two, and not too idealistic to be unaware that I was entering a difficult profession and starting work at a difficult school.

My first two days were both training days. I didn't know anyone, and had nothing to talk about anyway, especially since there were no children present and there was no teaching to be done. I had no shared experiences, no funny stories and no right to grumble about my lot like everyone else did. They didn't grumble about my lot. They didn't know anything about my lot. What I meant was that they grumbled about their lot. I couldn't agree with them when they rolled their eyes or complained about a particularly problematic pupil. What did I know?

To make matters worse I had to make the journey to school by train. People assumed that this was because, having just completed my PGCE teaching qualification, I was broke. Broke I was, but not for that reason. My impecunious state had more to do with an unwise property decision than with my recent studies. I had bought a house in the notorious Callon Estate in Preston two years earlier, assuming that if I left my neighbours alone, they would leave me alone.

It seemed fairly logical to me but I had not given any thought to the true nature of my new neighbourhood, taking its pleasant, tidy surroundings at face value and not realising that it had only just been renovated in preparation for the next round of mutilation inflicted upon it by some of those who lived there. That people would destroy the place in which they lived was beyond my experience, or that they would deliberately make it terrifying and lawless. I just didn't get it and still don't. We suffered abuse, theft, criminal damage and threats simply because we didn't fit in. It was the sort of place where taxing your car was considered snobbery.

Calling the police only made things worse, drawing attention to yourself as a law-abiding weirdo. It wasn't worth the bother. On one occasion, after we had been threatened by a mob outside our house, a police constable paid us a visit and told us 'that *we* should live and let live'. It was a tremendously useful piece of advice and we thanked him profusely.

Things culminated in both our cars being set on fire as they sat on our driveway. I will never forget the sight of the ethereal orange flicker of flames on the bedroom curtains and the crackling of burning plastic. I pulled the curtains open to see our cars engulfed in flames with spirals of cloying smoke twisting into the night air. A gang of children stood on the street corner and watched, but someone had at least called the Fire Service, who arrived within minutes and extinguished the flames. Pity was etched on their faces as they spoke to us later, but no one could really help. And that was why, in a roundabout sense, I got the train to work.

We moved out whilst I was on my teacher training and my wife her first year of teaching at a school in Chorley. Our first house was boarded up so that no one could break in and hurt themselves and then we tried to sell it. Strangely, no one was all that eager to buy a boarded-up semi in the centre of one of Lancashire's worst housing estates, but eventually it went for ten thousand pounds less than I had paid for it. I was in negative equity. My first year at Collegiate was spent without a car and without a wage as we tried to repay the debt I had incurred.

We moved into a flat in a block where I had a part-time job as a security guard and, as an interesting footnote, were visited by the same policeman who had spoken to us about the destruction of our cars in Callon, when our replacement car was also set on fire. Yes, another car was set on fire. You read that correctly.

I almost felt sorry for that car. When we still lived in Callon we had deliberately parked it well away from the house so that no one would realise it was ours. Despite this precautionary measure it got broken into regularly and in the end the door locks didn't really function properly. Following our move to the flat we used a garage for the poor old thing until my wife bought a new car and I became its proud owner. Unfortunately, this meant parking it on the street, but I made sure that it was visible from the flat. Until one night it wasn't.

'Diane, the car's gone', I said, mildly alarmed.

'Where?'

'Don't know'.

Later I saw the familiar flicker of flames from behind the wall of the community centre.

'The car's back', I said and indeed it was. At least it settled the argument of what joyriders do with your car when they have finished with it: they bring it back and set fire to it.

For a couple of weeks I had been a motorist, but now it was back to the train, waiting on the wind-blown platform each morning, my heart a-flutter with despondency.

Anyway, where was I? Oh yes, my morning routine. My alarm clock is the type that has a light that comes on dimly and gets brighter and brighter, gently stirring you from slumber to wakefulness without the jarring cacophony of an audible alarm. You wake up feeling relaxed and refreshed. Well, that's the theory. In all fairness it does wake me up and I don't miss the sound of an alarm clock at all, but the 'refreshed' effect seemed to wear off after a few weeks of use. Now I just wake up feeling as if I haven't even been to sleep – just like everyone else.

This morning was no different. I lay beneath the covers forcing my mind to trawl through the day I had in prospect, breaking it down into period one, period two and so on, giving each of them a rough dread rating. My day had nothing to recommend it really: angst, controversy, dispute, rudeness, all bundled together in an unpleasant catalogue of future events from which I would derive no satisfaction. The die was cast before I had even opened my eyes, unless by some miracle those children who would make my day so unpleasant all truanted in concert. It was a faint hope, or less than that even.

The worst lesson would be period five. In the days before my ability to instil and maintain discipline vanished, I prided myself on taking difficult-to-handle pupils into my class just to give other teachers a break. I had taken this one step further this year by asking for all the 'naughties' to be put into this particular class, which was a bottom set. The logic was that by taking the bulk of badly behaved children and placing them in one class, which was destined to achieve very little in any case, I would at least give my colleagues a fighting chance with their classes. It was a good idea... except that it wasn't really. Behaviour was in serious decline; lawlessness was in the ascendancy. I had flattered myself into thinking that I could at least contain these children's worst excesses, not allowing my recent experiences to temper my judgement. Maybe at one time I could have succeeded with the little mission I had set myself, but no longer.

I had effectively poisoned my own chalice, given myself a concentrated dose of unmanageable lunacy

– and a very unedifying spectacle it made too. There is nothing I like less than being tangibly not in control, except being seen to be such. To stand at the front of a classroom and be roundly ignored, mocked and reviled, is a terrible feeling that transcends mere disappointment. For your class to behave not just as if you weren't there, but as if they were under instruction to act like savages and for you to be completely powerless, is an utterly miserable and humiliating experience. You certainly feel like you're not doing your job, and that can be a very lonely feeling.

Even allowing for all that, even with my expectations so low, this period five turned out worse than any other I had known.

There was no space to queue outside the room, so even if the pupils had felt like doing so, they couldn't have queued in an orderly fashion. My only hope was that I might open the door to a *controllable* mob. It had never been any other way simply because of the physical location of the room, the door crammed into the furthest corner of an isolated corridor. Whereas some teachers might attempt to gain order before their class had even entered the room, this was not an option for me. Instead I got them in, behind their desks, books and pens out (if they had managed to bring such things, of course) and then tried to bring about some semblance of order. It *was* possible – or it had been – but nowadays I had to settle for less. My style of teaching was now compromised beyond the point where it was actually worth carrying on. Without order, teaching is impossible. When order becomes impossible...

The first indications of the rot had occurred maybe two years previously, when I had mentored a student teacher. My instruction to him was not to shout to gain order but to stand patiently and wait for it to come – a tactic which I normally used with a fair amount of success. Once your pupils realised that you were waiting for them to desist, they generally did just that. However, something had changed and I couldn't quite figure out what. I watched the young teacher, doing just as I had instructed, but the expected hush never came even though I was in the room with him. Eventually we settled the class by other means, but I was disconcerted.

Throughout his teaching practice, which lasted until Christmas, he struggled with the children's behaviour – not too unexpected in the case of a student – but once he'd left I found that I was having almost as much difficulty when I picked my classes back up. My powers were on the wane.

For answers, I looked at those things that had changed – principally the layout of my room – for I felt that *I* had not undergone any change at all. My room had been an old-fashioned school lab with wooden benches, square sinks and gas taps that sprang from the desktops like stunted metal shrubs. The layout was good, especially since my desk was on a podium at the front of the room. On either side of that podium there was a door. One led to the corridor and the other to the prep room, which served as the science staff's tea room. Strategically placed between the two I had control of who entered and, more importantly, who left... and generally no one did unless it was at my behest.

The only real problem was that my gas supply had been inoperable for about two or three years, meaning that experiments involving Bunsen burners were out, but apart from that the room was good and serviceable. With the refurbishment came a rearrangement which meant my new desk was moved to the side of the room, no longer on a podium. I was noticeably hemmed in by a computer desk, and my pupils were, for the most part, arranged on one huge 'squared off C'-shaped desk. This created a barrier between them and me and gave them easy access to the door should they wish to escape, an option which they increasingly took rather an endure an hour of science. The decision to alter the room's layout was taken by the school's management, although they had been advised against it for a number of practical reasons. I was however, consulted about the colour.

'What colour would you like your walls?', asked the Bursar.

'Orange', I replied.

'Well, they're going to be blue', she responded.

'Right I'll have them blue then.'

It was ever thus on the thorny issue of 'consultation'. The staff were always consulted about the big decisions that affected the school, but I don't recall their suggestions being given serious consideration. That did not alter the fact that they had been consulted of course.

And so, I faced every day with my new room and its blue walls, hemmed in by my desk, confronted with a horde of children, all seated at one long table which made a seating plan worthless. I had a projector that was connected to my computer, and on a number of occasions I could get it to work so that I was able to show presentations to the class. Sadly, my new layout meant that I had to stand between the projector and the screen in order to operate the equipment. I wondered if anyone had given any thought whatsoever to the organisation of my room. It certainly wasn't apparent if they had...

At first, I assumed that my problems stemmed from the change in the room itself, but that was only part of it. Maybe it was coincidence but the discipline that I had worked so hard to establish was suddenly gone as if someone had flicked a switch marked 'begin chaos'. There was a definite change and once it began there seemed to be no way of turning things back – I couldn't switch it off again.

A loss of authority is hard to overcome. A general who loses a battle, a surgeon who loses a patient, a solicitor who loses a case... well, these things happen of course but one's reputation doesn't always recover. Just supposing the view that children took of me was that, 'he's fair but don't cross him' – that's what I would have liked and, although I might flatter myself, I think that that is what I had achieved. And then, without any obvious reason, it changed to something less respectful than that. In that way a new generation or cohort of pupils see that same teacher as an ineffectual idiot whose ideas are irrelevant. It is the new idea which sticks, previous conceptions discarded.

So, I knew that it would be that sort of day, even before my feet had touched down on the cold bedroom floor. I knew what I was up against – maybe not in detail, but all the essential ingredients were known to me. Of course, one might argue that forewarned is forearmed, but that only holds true if there is a viable defence against the incipient assault; faced with hopelessness, all the stoicism and never-say-die attitude counts for nought.

The bulk of the day went by in a blur of humour, ill-will, malice, deceit and perhaps resignation to one's fate. Maybe some child happened to learn something that stood them in good stead for the next phase of their life... but I wouldn't put money on it. You have to ask yourself if anyone really needs to know how they breathe or why they do so. Intercostal muscles, the diaphragm, alveoli, respiration – it's all very well but not knowing what these things do, or what they are, or where they can be found, doesn't stop them from doing it, being what they are or being where they are. In short you will not stop breathing simply because you don't understand the process. If you were destined to become a doctor or a nurse then it's different but I rarely encountered anyone whose realistic ambition was to join the medical profession.

I say 'realistic ambition' because there was no shortage of the other type – unrealistic ambition. Many children had seemingly decided upon careers that were well beyond their reach. Increasingly, when asked, many said that they wanted to be forensic scientists because of the plethora of US shows depicting the exciting life that would be. That these same children, for the most part, would leave school with two or three GCSEs if they were exceedingly fortunate, did nothing to stifle their ambition. In some circumstances this might be considered laudable but in these circumstances it was merely laughable. Teachers could have been more honest, of course, and told the relevant children the truth about their future – that it didn't

15

amount to much more than the miserable struggle that they already experienced – but the problem was one of motivation. Why would a child, just supposing they were so motivated in the first place, make the effort to learn if they knew that they could aspire to seasonal work in a hotel or theme park and nothing more?

So, I suppose we were all guilty of a certain degree of ambiguity when it came to our pupils' job prospects. It was a sort of conspiracy of silent acquiescence, a failure to inform… certainly not malicious but perhaps lazy and harmful. Why shouldn't a low ability child hope to be a vet? Except, of course, that one day they will learn the real extent of their personal job market, that's why. How do you tell them that they'll be lucky to get a job in the local cat food factory, let alone putting suppositories up a dog's back end, and what sort of response can you reasonably expect from them if you do? Hardly motivational, is it?

Such was the nature of the job: reinforcing hopelessness, putting a gloss on failure and calling it something else. Not in every case of course, but there was no escaping the relentless pursuit of academic excellence using profoundly unsuitable human stock. Perhaps that's at the root of the problem to some extent; certainly, schools are packed with children who have progressed beyond their viable educational limit. 'Value added', was a popular euphemism used to describe children who failed their exams less miserably than was expected.

I could paraphrase Sun Tzu, who created the military maxim, 'you must reinforce success and starve failure'. We reinforced failure too often, entering children for exams on subjects at which they had peaked at primary school. No wonder some of them railed against the apparent stupidity of the education system and everyone involved in it. That's not to say that the behaviour some of them displayed from time to time and with increasing frequency was forgivable, just that it is possible to detect its origins.

So that was the nature of my job, day in, day out, interspersed with moments when the clouds of ignorance parted and a few rays of wisdom shone through, to be absorbed by those children who were prepared to work for their own future.

Period five, Monday afternoon. Not the worst lesson on the timetable but not the best either (worst and best being relative terms of course). It hadn't been a great day but I had survived with my sanity intact... although I'm not saying that that's a good thing entirely. Who wants to be sane when surrounded by insanity? I could have taken comfort from my apparent success but I didn't because I knew that the worst was yet to come. I felt beleaguered, trapped by the knowledge that all my experience, my accrued wisdom (such as it was) and my supposed authority counted for nothing. I was a good teacher stripped of the apparatus needed to do my job – the ability to control my class. I was at their mercy and I felt this vulnerability very keenly before the bell had even sounded to end lunch. Period five.

The last time I had felt so powerless was back on the Callon Estate. It was the day that I moved out forever. Diane was staying with her family in York for the weekend and I had stayed behind because I had a part-time job as a security guard which required me to work Saturdays or Sundays. It wasn't long after the cars had been burnt out so I wasn't feeling at all comfortable about being in my house. For me it was not the case that 'an Englishman's house is his castle' and not just because I'm not an Englishman. My house made me feel more vulnerable if anything, perhaps because those who sought to make my existence a miserable one knew exactly where to find me.

Glancing out of the bedroom window, I saw a car drive past. It was a non-descript saloon car – I can't remember the type – but it was going very slowly and had three or four young men inside, all of whom seemed to be on the lookout for something. Perhaps it was just paranoia on my part. We'd had threats, had things stolen and of course the cars... Now this. My mind took a leap of its own volition; these young men were looking for me, or at least the house in which I lived. Fourteen years on from that day as I write this I realise that maybe they were doing no such thing, although I have little doubt that they were up to no good but then...? Well, back then my brain offered up only one possibility and I sought, but was unable to find, an alternative. Quite simply they were here for me. Maybe they weren't going to do anything in broad daylight but they were going to do something. The car edged out of view, but I remained almost paralysed with fear until it returned, very slowly, maybe a minute later. I rang Diane, packed a bag and moved out. Neither of us spent another night in that house.

Period five. As the last traces of a discordant bell echoed off to oblivion, we raised ourselves from the blue uncomfortable chairs that lined our little prep room. This was the science teacher's bolt-hole, where we could have a hot drink, a biscuit and a moan. Sometimes we might have just the biscuit and not the hot drink or vice versa, but invariably we had a moan, perhaps because despair at the hopelessness of our situation was the only thing which we really shared. My room adjoined the prep room but once I crossed the threshold all the comfort and security that could be found there was gone.

There is no place to hide in a classroom, at least not if you happen to be the teacher. Down through the years various pupils had managed to secrete themselves into cupboards for reasons of tiresome hilarity, but for the hapless teacher it's your show and once you have admitted those children into your domain you have to stand there and deliver the act regardless of the audience's opinion thereof. The first phase of the procedure was to let them into the room, uncomplicated in theory, but in reality a myriad things could go wrong. I always chose to greet my class as cheerily as I could manage, with what passed for a smile and some verbal expression of my delight at seeing them again. Was I lying when I said how nice it was to see them again? Possibly. It certainly was insincere but it did reflect in some obscure way how I felt things ought to be. If my job was to teach these children and to help improve their lives, then why wouldn't I be glad to see them and they me?

As usual I had only a few pupils at the door, most of them relatively eager to get on with the lesson. These were the handful for whom, in other circumstances, there might have been some hope. They came in obediently, quietly, saying hello as they passed, and then went to their places, retrieving the few items that they required for the lesson; their book, a pen and a pencil. This was how it should be but sadly it would not last. I could have started the lesson, made the most of my attentive little gathering, except for one thing: the rest of the class, the unruly majority who had yet to appear. They would be on their way, ejected from the toilets having hastily dumped their cigarettes with a watery hiss, or on the rampage around the school, the last of their lunchtime e-number energy surging through their veins like adrenaline. I looked at my class and then at the door, propped open in readiness by the metal bin that so few of them ever used. I kept despair at bay with positive thoughts: 'perhaps there'll be a fire drill, or even better a real fire, and we can all go and stand in the all-weather pitches for an hour'. I didn't ask for much.

It was too early in the year for my little 'calm before the storm group' to realise just how doomed their education was. They probably thought that I would eventually get control of the class and lead them all on some sort of modest journey of enlightenment, but that time was actually long gone. The absent portion of the class – the majority – comprised the naughties that I had on my class list and the ones that I had volunteered to take in my attack of fatalistic altruism. When they appeared, in some sort of disjointed hurricane of disaffection, the lesson would be over in any meaningful sense. The well-behaved children hadn't given up yet, but they would.

Five or six minutes had passed and the lesson had gone precisely nowhere. 'Good teachers', of which I was seemingly no longer one, always had a starter activity of the board for the class to begin whilst things settled down. I asked my group to begin the activity and dutifully they did so, although I think we shared a knowledge that their efforts were going to be stifled imminently... and so it proved, as the first of the remainder launched himself through the door, pretending that he had been thrown in. Much better that he had come in normally and then pretended to be thrown out, never to return, but you can't have everything. Another miscreant followed soon afterwards and they at once began arguing, both out of breath and excited, but not due to the prospect of their science lesson.

A minute or so later three girls came in, chatting in an animated fashion. One of them scowled at me but none offered any form of apology for their lateness. They sat in roughly the right place, each one still wearing their coat and with their bags on the desk in front of them as if in defence. Their bags were bright, open-topped shopping bags, the type that was in vogue for young ladies at school. Despite their large capacity there was no guarantee that they might contain the appropriate books or a pencil case. A tube of fake tan, sanitary towels, cigarettes, a can of Coke and a folder for their favourite BTec course, yes... anything else – probably not. Many children habitually asked their teachers for pens or rulers, even when they actually had managed to bring these exotic items to school, simply because they were too lazy to look for them in their own bags.

They thought nothing of chewing, losing, breaking, stealing or throwing the pen they were loaned. To refuse to lend a pen as a point of principle invariably elicited the response, 'well, I can't do my work then', as if it were actually the teacher's fault that this impasse had been reached. Often it was simply easier to hand over a pen so that they could scribble their notes down. Pen or no pen, the impact upon their education was basically the same: if a child is prepared to argue with their teacher about the fact that they have to make some effort with regards to their own education, then you are wasting your time with them...and that's just how it was, day in, day out.

Another few girls filed in, quietly and guiltily bringing a vague smell of cigarette smoke with them. Smoking was one of the few things that seemed likely to incur some sort of punishment from the senior management and yet it was essentially a victimless crime, the children only really hurting themselves. If you reported them for telling you to 'fuck off', you might get asked what you had done to provoke this response, but if you reported them for smoking then quite possibly they might find themselves in the inclusion unit – a terrifying prospect, in which the young criminal had to work in silence in a small room for an entire day. How mere flesh could withstand such a measure was beyond me.

Soon I had what could nominally be described as 'a class' in front of me, although the word 'class' implies a group of people brought together with a common desire to learn. Trying to apply that definition to the sundry malcontents assembled in this rather haphazard fashion was stretching things. Now that they were finally here, they chatted, sang, ate, argued, threw things at each other or fought, anything that excluded any possibility of learning really. Yet my original little group hung on hopefully in case the opportunity to get down to the lesson actually occurred. It was their imploring looks that hurt me most, that and the gradual erosion of faith in their teacher.

I rarely shouted nowadays. To do so was seen as weak, ineffective and, worst of all, non-child-centric. The children needed to be stimulated, engaged, valued. They had to understand what their own personal targets were. They had to understand the aims and objectives of the lesson and to be reminded of when they had met these. They had also to improve their literacy but not be expected to read or write very much. They had to be involved in lots of short learning activities that were interactive and challenging, but not overly so. They had to discuss, argue, work in groups, produce displays. There was an endless, unfathomable list of things they had to do and it was for me to lead them into this brave new world of learning; to lead them to educational utopia.

Whereas, in fact, I couldn't even get them to shut up.

I looked at them with – and I know that this is a recurring theme – but I looked at them with despair. Perhaps mild despair, if that emotion can be sub-divided into categories. Half of me thought, 'why should I care?', half thought, 'how humiliating'. Yet another half felt great sadness for the small group who clung to hope and another half felt depressed and useless. I know that's four halves in total, but I had enough emotions for two people.

Had I never experienced the ability to teach effectively and keep control of the children in my class I might not have been so bothered. Some teachers never possess that certain indefinable quality which makes them successful in the classroom, and for them their entire career is just a battle. They are the ones who shout and scream. They berate their pupils and eventually learn to shout above the noise in the hope that something they say will stick. I had never been such a teacher and even now I refused to talk over the top of my class, which sadly meant that I barely talked at all sometimes. It was the knowledge that I had once been in control that made my current plight hard to take. Had that never been the case then I would at least have had ten years to come to terms with being hopelessly excluded from the teaching process.

If I could have somehow detached myself from the lesson just for a moment I might have been able to take comfort from the fact that it couldn't descend into farce, albeit simply because that was how it had begun: as farce. It would have been an illusory crutch however, because things took a turn for the worse in what would become one of the defining moments of my life.

Chapter Two

The beginning of the end

I'll call them Rebecca and Debbie because that's close enough. One of these girls I had taught the previous year when she had been in year eight, and our relationship then had been based upon grudging acceptance that we existed in different worlds, neither of which necessarily impinged upon the other. Outwardly we co-existed but such was the vastness of the gulf in our respective experience that we were almost strangers. It was a relationship that transcended mere 'having nothing in common-ness'. We were not antagonistic towards each other, but ambivalent. I don't think she could really understand why I wasn't more lax and familiar, something she may have been used to from other members of staff.

The other girl, the one I am calling Debbie, was known to me, but I had never previously taught her. Both girls frequently displayed challenging behaviour, a euphemism beloved of management. Ordinary teachers, the ones who daily had to combat 'challenging behaviour', described it and its perpetrators in other terms, many of which had a strongly Anglo-Saxon flavour to them. On her own, Rebecca's sullenness had a poignant quality to it, as if her dislike of school and its apparatus was natural and deserved. In company she felt obliged to adhere to a stereotype in which she loudly railed against the system.

I am sure to this day that she knew her teachers were there to help her, and that school offered her opportunities that could change her life, but her background was such that only by fighting the system could she get the sort of respect she craved. Don't ask me why it's like that for some children, but all too often it is. Her friend Debbie was an altogether different proposition however, and in tandem they could make a teacher's life a misery. Debbie, it seemed, rarely let slip any of the outward signs of common humanity that she undoubtedly possessed. She was resolutely anti-everything, her antipathy boundless. To say that she was hard to please was the mother and father of all understatements, a fact which was amply displayed via the medium of a permanent scowl.

Whilst her aggression and supreme disillusionment was and perhaps still is a tragedy of sorts, it was also very hard on the unfortunate teacher who tried to communicate with and assist the poor girl. That her unhappiness with life was taken out on the very people who offered her the chance to bring about an improvement in that respect was unfair, but typical of the fundamental flaw at the heart of Britain's education system.

Sad to say, her presence rarely brightened anyone's day in the same way that her absence did. She was an inveterate latecomer, her poor timekeeping a badge of pride worn like an aura. That she was late for every lesson had the double disadvantage of wooing her teachers into the fond hope that she wouldn't turn up at all and of destroying what might have been an adequate lesson when she did so. Nevertheless, I always tried to be pleased to see her, if only because doing so might possibly spur her on to performing acts of reasonable behaviour.

In theory were I to express my displeasure at her arrival then I would only have myself to blame if she then decided to act up, but the reality was it made no difference. At least I could say that I had tried to set the correct tone for the lesson, but that was all. I was damned no matter what approach I took unless I congratulated her for getting to the lesson at all. Even then she might view that as sarcasm.

Rebecca and Debbie entered the room like a whirlwind of fake tan and expletives. With regard to the former it seemed that orange-ness was fashionable. Fake tan found its way from these girls faces onto their shirt collars, riming it with crusty gunk. With regard to the latter they barely even *attempted* to moderate their language in the presence of someone who might theoretically be offended by it. Actually, I was only really offended by their lack of respect and by the fact that they didn't even consider the possibility that I or another member of the class might be offended.

I was dismayed, concerned, but not surprised. There wasn't a lot I could do about it. The only punishment available to me was a detention, the implementation of which would cause me greater problems and solve nothing. Firstly, any slight hope I might have entertained about securing their cooperation for the remainder of the lesson would be gone, and secondly, they simply wouldn't turn up. They weren't afraid of the consequences of their behaviour and I was simply an irrelevance. All of which goes some way towards explaining what happened next. Nearly two years later I was able to read about the ensuing 'difficulty' in the Sunday Telegraph, so forgive me if I skip ahead for a moment. The headline read, 'A schoolgirl simulated a sex act in class – and the teacher who disciplined her was fired. Now he has been vindicated'. At the time, of course I was viewing the unfolding horror in quite a different way, not imagining how things would spiral out of control.

'During a science lesson with a class of bottom set thirteen-year olds at Collegiate High School in Blackpool,

one girl, a known troublemaker, threw herself into the lap of a startled girl sitting nearby and began simulating a lewd sex act. Her teacher, David Roy, was horrified. When the youngster finally stood up, she wandered around the classroom, disrupting the lesson. Eventually she slumped down upon a table, turning her back on her teacher. Mr Roy was not prepared to talk to the girl's back. Nor was he willing to let her disrupt the class. "So, I moved the table, which was big and heavy, and in a dramatic gesture – what I would call and exaggerated fashion – she fell off," he explains.'

(Extract taken from an article written by Rebecca Lefort, reproduced with kind permission from the Sunday Telegraph, 29th August 2010)

The table was an adjustable affair with a mechanism to raise and lower the top so that children in wheelchairs could sit there comfortably. Moving it was a really a job for two people, and yet 'Debbie' managed to fall from it after I had given it a sharp tug. It had barely shifted. Nothing else I had done got her attention, and she ignored me with a determination that would have been commendable had she applied it to her studies (or her manners). Now she wailed that she was injured, and her friends castigated me for my actions.

Swiftly recovering from her injuries, she left the room, shouting at me and telling me that, 'she was going to get me done'. I didn't doubt her. I was now a villain, her story given credence where there was none. My stomach knotted at once. I knew that there would be an automatic assumption of guilt on my part. Her actions could all be excused because she was a child, whereas I was culpable because I was an adult. This was a well-established trend in schools, none more so than the one at which I taught. However, I had no idea just how far events would take me in the coming year.

Returning home that afternoon, shaken and ashen-faced, I wrote my version of events. I knew that this matter would be investigated, not because there was any need but because that's just how it was. The following day I was summoned by the deputy head who informed me that a complaint had been made and that an official investigation was to be carried out. He expressed his regret that such a course of action was necessary. I shrugged and said, 'not to worry' or words to that effect, but days later other events overtook me.

It was my sister who delivered the news that my father had died for the second time. We had been estranged for over twenty years, during which time I assume that his mental health had been in serious decline. Never the most likeable or stable of men, it seemed that the excesses of his lifestyle had finally rounded on him. Prior to this he had somehow 'staged' his own death via rumour and supposition. To paraphrase Mark Twain, 'rumours of his death were greatly exaggerated', on this occasion at least. The tale reached my sister – also estranged from him – and from her to me. I didn't know how to feel really. He and I had certainly not been close and yet he was still my dad, or had been. There would be no reconciliation now. But it's a confusing concept because he wasn't dead of course, although I did not realise that at the time. Not only was he dead (so I thought) but he was buried and there was no funeral, no arrangements to make and no will to fight over; whoever had inherited his sock full of two pence pieces, it certainly wasn't me.

To make matters worse, I had found myself forced to tell the deputy head (she eventually became the headteacher and my nemesis, some years later) of his demise one day when she dragged me into her office to ask why I always looked so miserable. My truthful response could have been that it was due to the fact that I worked at Collegiate High School, but instead of that I told her that my father had died. She was mortified at her intrusion into my private and entirely unfounded grief.

Days later I discovered, again via my sister, that he was not dead at all, but I never quite found the right moment to tell the deputy head of his newly acquired status: that of 'undead'. It was awkward. Most people are declared formally deceased, not formerly deceased – it's usually a much more permanent state than that. Overnight I had gone from being semi-orphaned to having a full parental complement, with no adequate means of explaining how this had happened.

The embarrassing upshot was that when he finally did die, I needed to ask for time off for the funeral in Northern Ireland. My obvious predicament was the fact that as far as anyone was concerned, my father had been dead for years. How, therefore, did I broach the subject of his second death?

Upon my return to school a week later, my father definitively buried, I found that the incident with Debbie had been referred to the police, social services and the child-protection agency, none of which wanted to take matters any further. An internal investigation concluded that any injury that the girl might have sustained had been caused accidentally. I was exonerated of any blame. *Exonerated.* Remember that word.

Chapter Three

Calm before the storm

I returned to work but some of the worst elements of that particular class, including Debbie, were moved on, the official verdict being that I had bitten off more than I could chew. My professional life continued in the chaotic manner to which I had become accustomed. I tried to do everything that I was instructed to do, no matter how hopeless it seemed. Maybe it was as a consequence of my years in the army but I simply couldn't let things go. If the Head said she wanted a crackdown on excess jewellery, for instance, then I tried to ensure that the pupils in my care conformed. Personally, I would rather have had dealings with polite children whose features were completely obscured by studs, bangles, bracelets and sovereign rings, than rude, unkind children whose one saving grace was to be jewellery-free, but my view was that you didn't have to like the rules, just enforce them.

In that respect I was my own worst enemy. Rules that some other teachers ignored, I tried to implement. Turning a blind ear and a deaf eye was common practice and it was no wonder that this was so when the penalties for upholding the rules could be so great. Who really wanted that lonely confrontation with a girl ordered to remove her make-up? Those were the occasions when one realised that the teacher was an isolated, powerless individual rather than the member of a close-knit team whose actions were sanctioned and supported by their managers. I tended to fight the school's battles on my own, not as the spearhead of a great movement aiming for conformity.

Many children – generally the ones who it was necessary to confront – were unashamedly defiant. It might seem as if their every action was designed to cause an issue that would escalate into an incident once the hapless teacher tried to sort it out. It wasn't just a case of trying to enforce unpopular rules, although that was part of it – the biggest problem was children deliberately flouting the rules knowing that it would create disruption. In that case the subsequent argument was unavoidable, and reason was pointless…

Back in the days when I had effective discipline, I had always taken other teachers' naughty children from them if required. This simple expedient – removing a pupil from their audience and placing them with another class, often another year group – worked brilliantly, and I had resolved never to turn away any pupil. Even now I still accepted misbehaving pupils into my class despite the fact that I was having problems of my own. On occasions I had even taken half a class from another teacher and put them in my room during one of my free lessons, something that I didn't mind doing but which was nevertheless a considerable bind, especially if they decided to act up again. Sometimes I had to stand by my door to dissuade them from just walking out, and in doing so I became a prisoner in my own classroom, or more precisely, that corner of my classroom.

That was one of the big problems that was getting bigger – actually keeping children in the classroom. The act of storming out had gone from an isolated occurrence to a regular event, almost a right. The fact that the children were actually locked in the school (all exterior doors were locked during school hours) created more problems than it solved, because whereas previously upon making their escape they would go home or off around Blackpool, now they could only remain in school causing mayhem.

The Headteacher, Ms Fennel, had informed us that children were not to be let out of lessons except in a very limited range of circumstances. She had also informed us that if a child tried to leave your lesson you were to let them go. There is an obvious dichotomy here. Trying to implement such instructions was somewhere between problematic and impossible. Our rule book was a collection of grey areas, leavened with contradiction and hopeless advice but like the emperor's new clothes nobody said anything; to do so was to invite scrutiny and 'support' for one's teaching. You couldn't go far wrong if you remember that it was *your fault*. Whatever happened *you* were to blame.

For such occurrences as absence from lessons or prematurely leaving a lesson we had, as previously mentioned, the feeble deterrent of detention. In addition, we had a computerised registration system known as BROMCOM. At the start of each lesson we took a register on the computer which was then electronically transferred to the main office. Thus, at any given time it was possible to see who was in school but absent from class, right? I'm not sure. For some reason we also had to send a note to the office with a list of children who were absent. This caused disruption to the lesson of course, involved removing a pupil from the lesson to actually take the note, and didn't allow for the fact that in the intervening period half the missing children were likely to have turned up. I frequently highlighted the failings of this ludicrous system at staff meetings, but no-one cared. Rarely did anyone agree with me openly.

Another problem was that some teachers only sent the register once their class had all turned up. They might wait fifteen or twenty minutes to facilitate this process whereas I only gave my pupils a few minutes to get from their previous lesson to mine. Statistically therefore, I had a greater rate of lateness or absence than these other teachers, which reflected poorly upon me for some reason, when in fact I was merely being diligent. Again, no-one cared. As I said, I was my own worst enemy. I came to realise that the instructions we were given by the Head were for show and not to be acted upon. Just so long as everything could be contained within the walls of the school it would be okay.

It was far from okay.

For some reason I didn't give up, suffering as I did from what might be termed dogged stupidity. There certainly seemed to be some inability on my part to admit defeat even though (to drag the analogy a little further) I had been overrun, if not massacred. That's not to say that I didn't witness something of the sort every day: an educational massacre.

We were in the longest term, but it did at least have a joyful conclusion, that being Christmas. Christmas was great for two reasons: schools shut for two weeks and Jesus was born so that we might have eternal life. To be honest, being a shallow sort of person, it was the two weeks' holiday that appealed to me most. Eternal life didn't really grab me; things would have to pick up considerably before I opted to live forever. In the last few weeks of term I was given a cover lesson that would have enormous repercussions for me, giving impetus to a process in which I was going to lose not only my job, but my career and my good name too.

***

Generally, teachers were given about one cover lesson per week and it was something of an unlucky dip. Everyone did roughly the same number of covers per year, although some thought that they did many more than everyone else. A colleague of mine used to claim that he did more than his share of cover lessons and yet when the statistics were printed off for the purposes of stopping the staff from moaning about their lot, it transpired that he actually did amongst the fewest. It's all to do with perceptions. You only really see what's happening to you.

What *was* true and terribly obvious, was that some teachers, through their own appalling attendance rate, *created* more covers than their colleagues. One female teacher in particular was well known for taking exactly the number of self-certifiable sickness days she could have. Year in, year out she did this, her name featuring heavily on the dreaded cover list. Eventually, in one of the few admirable acts she ever performed, the Head had the doorway to this teacher's room bricked up during a protracted absence. It was a peerless statement of intent and that teacher's resignation, mourned by no-one, followed soon after. Her room was knocked through into another and a computer suite created, using the lavish amounts of money thrown at the school and essentially wasted.

I digress. This particular cover involved me taking a year nine class whose teacher was off with a fractured eyebrow or something equally serious. Some staff would have dragged themselves in to work even if they'd had multiple amputations the previous day, in the mistaken belief that the world would stop turning if they didn't show their face. Others would confine themselves to bed for a week at the first sign of split ends or a sprained nostril. I assume that most of my colleagues displayed a degree of common sense when it came to sick leave, but they were reviled anyway if their absence generated a cover lesson for a non-absent colleague when they were expecting to be free.

The classroom in this instance was next to the staffroom and the cover occurred during period five, the final session of the school day. I made my way to the room and took up station next to the door ready to greet my students. I waited and waited. Then I sat down behind the teacher's desk. Everything was going well, particularly as I had no actual class with which to contend. All in all, it was a very agreeable situation and one which I was loath to end by doing anything foolish like trying to locate the missing pupils. Truth was, they were somewhere, they hadn't just ceased to be.

I checked the cover list in the staffroom, but all the details were correct, the room number, the period, the absent teacher, the name of the stand-in teacher (me) and the date. Everything was in order but there were no children. I returned to my seat not terribly concerned. I could go and look for them, but it was a big school and I didn't know where to start. Not only that but I wouldn't necessarily recognise them even if I found them. Clearly someone was looking after them. Had that not been the case then they would have been on the rampage. One minute more and I was going to take to my heels and find somewhere to hide.

Sadly, but inevitably, an emissary was sent from the class to find me before my simple escape plan reached fruition. The class, it transpired, were in the library, as was the case every week, although no-one bothered me with this minor detail. They were in the care of a teaching assistant and it was she who informed me that their regular teacher, who happened to be an assistant headteacher, normally took half of the group down to the all-weather pitches to play football, whilst the others completed written work. Quite how this arrangement had ever come about was beyond me, but I was the lucky beneficiary on this occasion and took my little band of athletes outside for a highly educational kickabout. It was a relief to know that their usual teacher, who was paid a vastly greater sum than I, took their education so seriously. There can be little doubt that an afternoon game of football will have helped them all to secure gainful employment and made them into upstanding citizens.

The pitches were enclosed like tennis courts and marked out for various sports, the most arcane being lacrosse. The school was an alleged 'sports college' and pupils genuinely had to play lacrosse as part of the curriculum! It's so obscure that it doesn't even feature in the Olympics (and that now includes every sport known to humanity and some that probably don't really exist). Anyway, they weren't playing that, they were playing football, minus the rules. The pitches had floodlights but there was still enough daylight to see by. In the adjoining pitch a proper PE lesson was being conducted and I wondered if I was even qualified to oversee the half-arsed football debacle being played in front of me. There was nothing I could do about it of course.

Before very long the great sporting challenge ground to a halt. The teacher in the next court shouted across to me that I had an intruder of sorts, a pupil who had escaped from another lesson. I knew the boy but hadn't actually realised that he wasn't part of my group and so I instructed him to leave and return to his lesson. Without further ado he ignored me, so I tried again. He ignored me again. If anything, he ignored me more intently. He was one of the school's many loose cannons, doing what he pleased, going where he liked, and saying what he wanted to whomever he wanted to say it. Quite why he came to school was something of a mystery. The opportunities for doing precisely what he wanted were much greater on the outside than within the confines of school. Left to his own devices he would have been fine, in fact it would have been better all-round if my PE colleague hadn't said anything, but now I was forced to act, when a shrug of the shoulders would have sufficed and saved me a lot of aggro for the net result. Realising that he was not going to leave I asked one of the boys to kick the ball over to me.

The boy, whom I shall call John, had been in my class the previous year. We had got along well and I had actually moved him up a set because I was impressed with his attitude and his work... which made it all the more surprising when he refused to pass the ball to me. He was the only 'player' whose name I knew so I had picked him to take the ball out of play so that I could get rid of our extra man. I explained to John why I wanted the ball i.e. that it was just a temporary measure and that they would get it back when the other boy had left, but to my dismay he still refused to comply. John and I exchanged words, but eventually another boy tapped the ball over to me and I picked it up.

What had started as a simple kickabout was now some sort of incident, and it was set to get worse. No one could play football now, and they were none too happy about it. I, of course, was an unreasonable villain. The boy that I had been trying to get rid of had thankfully acquiesced, but I was now obliged to take a stand with John and I ordered him to return to the library with the other half of the group. Naturally he refused. Why should he accept that he had done anything wrong?

Eventually, after a protracted argument, and following some peer pressure from his mates who wanted to get on with their football, he agreed to stand next to me and not take part in the game. The others got the ball back and I once again tried to make John go back to his original lesson. He refused and told me that he didn't have to do what anyone told him, which in the context of this school was probably correct. The children were as aware as the staff that discipline was breaking down. They knew that there were no longer any meaningful consequences for their actions.

Grudgingly, I let him stand with me and we watched the game in tense silence. After a few minutes, when I gauged that he had calmed down a little, I tried a different approach to get my way – reason – but even that stalled immediately, and it was partly my fault. I asked John what he wanted to do when he left school and he replied that he wanted to be in the army, at which point I burst out laughing.

'But you've just told me that you don't have to do what anyone tells you', I said. 'Now you're saying you want to be in the army. Do you think that no-one's going to tell you what to do there?'

'I'll do what I'm told when I'm in the army', he said simply. I think that some part of him had realised what a ridiculous position he'd put himself in. I looked at John and shook my head. What, I wondered, was going on and how had we ended up in this situation? Why was it that I, someone who had demonstrated my humanity to this boy, was now his implacable foe?

But I knew the answer. It was symptomatic of the disease of dissent that had spread through the school. The initiative was being given over to the pupils and taken away from the staff. The pupils considered themselves to have so many rights that it didn't matter if they impinged upon the rights of others. The Head had told me during a subsequent meeting that it was no longer the case that teachers told pupils what to do and they simply did it, 'it's more to do with negotiation'. As things stood, I was nothing more than the latest victim of this lunatic culture. I wasn't really much of a negotiator.

John won that battle. Although his participation in the football was over, he had not returned to his class. However, rather than accepting defeat as I should have done, I decided that John would have a detention. I completed a slip of paper telling him that his detention would be for one hour after school the following Monday. He had more than the twenty-four hours' notice required, and I gave him the slip personally so that he couldn't claim he'd never received it. John was less than delighted but said nothing. It wasn't so simple, however, and we both knew it. It was virtually an unwritten rule that he would not attend and that I would lose the second heat of our struggle. If I kept on I could place him in a Faculty Detention which he would also not attend, and then it would be referred on until the process ran out of steam, with a sad inevitability. The only other thing I could do was to catch up with John at his last lesson on Monday and make sure that he stayed. This happened to be science with my friend and colleague Matthew Dodd, and he understood that I would be coming to him just before the bell went to make sure that John didn't forget to stay behind. What could go wrong?

John looked shocked by my presence, very much as if the game was up. I reminded him again that he was doing his detention, but he stated that he wasn't, and this pointless argument went back and forwards for some time with the rest of the class looking on. His angst filled the room like a suffocating gas. The atmosphere was toxic. John stood to leave the room with his classmates once the bell had gone but his way was blocked, and we got into another argument. I explained calmly to him that the best thing was for him to just do the detention. In the meantime, the class had left via an adjoining room, trailing out through a maze of stools and benches, half wanting to witness the outcome of our spat and half wanting to get home.

John ran into this room and tried to escape but the door had now been locked so he sprinted back in great distress, making his way for the door in front of which I stood. Everything happened in an instant. A mob of children had formed outside the room and were shouting at John telling him that he didn't have to do the detention. Only I stood between him and freedom. At a later date, when the first serious attempt at somehow criminalising my behaviour was being made, it was suggested that I had deliberately blocked his way. In fact, I was just standing in the most appropriate place, next to the door from where I could escort John to my room for his detention. Even if I had been blocking the door, then so what?

The racket and confusion were almost more than flesh could stand but I remained calm even when John gave me a two-handed push to clear me from his path. In a rare moment of mob co-ordination, the door was flung open and John charged headlong in a bid to escape. I reached for him and moments later we were both in the confined entrance to Matt's room, me holding John's lapels and him struggling like a large, captured fish.

Still I was calm. I tried to reason with him, but he got more and more angry, swearing, pushing, threatening. He began to sob just as two of my colleagues rounded the corner from the English department. They got a snap-shot view of the incident's final act. One of them urged me to release John and this I did. He ran off sobbing, not quite the tough nut he liked to portray, and I went downstairs, defeated. I wasn't exactly a broken man. I'd hate you to think that I crumbled at that point or any other, but I had an idea that this would go badly for me... and so it proved.

I had already taken a decision about my future but the timing couldn't have been worse. Nevertheless, I pressed on with my simple plan. My head of department had been in post for just over a year. He was a well-meaning man but completely at sea with his responsibilities and an easy target for our kids (He, like a great many others was subsequently forced out of his job). On several occasions I had helped him out with naughty children in his class, even taking them away during my free lessons. I didn't mind doing this, but it was a strange arrangement – he was supposed to be the overall arbiter of discipline within the faculty, not me. On this occasion however, I went to see him with a proposal about my position within the school. It was a difficult decision, but I felt that I had nowhere else to turn, no other option.

'I want to be considered to be a failing teacher', I said. Simon blinked and looked at me as if I had gone mad. He was sitting at his desk with the eager, talkative and duplicitous second-in-faculty next to him. No doubt they had been discussing matters of state. The second-in-faculty, Phil, gave his nervous, insincere laugh, but it was not a joke.

'I can't keep going with things as they are', I said by way of explanation. 'I want to be considered as a failing teacher'. I can't remember what reply was made, if any, but I went home at that point, agitated and despondent. I would remain that way for the next two years.

Chapter Four

Scrutiny

Within a few days I was summoned to the Head's office. This was certainly not unexpected. It was obvious that some sort of accusation against me would be made and that she would immediately get her knickers in a twist about it. Rather than getting the boy's parents in and giving him a good rollicking for his behaviour, I would be the one whose actions would come under scrutiny. The more you are seen to act that way – siding with pupils against the staff – the more children (some of them) will engineer these situations. With a headteacher who was afraid of the kids (and their parents, perhaps) but willing to take on the staff, this is an inevitable consequence. Teachers are generally reasonable and acquiescent, pupils frequently the opposite. The former are therefore soft targets.

Her room was a pokey affair, displaying all the character that she herself had i.e. none. The plain furnishings and bare walls complemented her personality well: simple, bland, unimaginative. Her expensive, made-to-look-cheap desk told the story of her life, bereft of photos of partner and children. She exuded loneliness. Her life was a bleak thing; all she had was her job and tragically she wasn't much good at it. She'd had more than one attempt at becoming the headteacher and been turned down before the departure of her predecessor, an idiot who blazed a trail of incompetence across the UK, going from one school to the next and leaving each one with dire problems.

Compared to him she seemed like a good bet, a safe pair of hands if nothing else, but those who had vetoed her appointment in the past had been right to do so. Whatever weakness they suspected was there all right.

Upon her predecessor's departure she had assumed temporary responsibility for the school and had at once turned his office into extra space for the office staff at reception. In effect, had a head other than her been appointed, they would have had no office to use! Thus, upon her permanent appointment to the post, she was confined to the little box room that had been hers as a deputy headteacher. I entered the room and she gave a toothy smile and said good morning, both of which were insincere. I sat and she got down to business at once. I was nauseated by her but never more so than when I knew I was in trouble.

'There has been a complaint made about an incident between you and John ******', she said. I nodded and didn't speak. She carried on. 'His mother is coming in tomorrow, so I'd like you to speak to her about it.' I nodded again and the meeting seemed to be at an end. It was that brief. Fennel had almost seemed to wash her hands of the matter, letting me sort it out with the parent – or was she throwing me to the wolves? She didn't ask me what had happened, nor did she suggest that I make a statement. I left the sad little room, feeling weary and disconsolate. Nothing in this strange school was ever as straightforward as it seemed, and I wondered where this meeting was going to lead. Why did I have to speak to the mother, exactly? Obviously, Fennel thought that I had something to explain, but what? And why did I have to explain myself anyway? In fact, the meeting never took place, but I was summoned to the Head's office two days later nevertheless.

Without much preamble she informed me that I was being sent home, and although she didn't use the phrase 'gardening leave', that is what it was; the last recourse of desperate headteachers with a 'problem' teacher. Although in one sense I was pleased to be going home I knew that this was a bad situation in which to find myself. Somehow, I sensed that events were unlikely to pan out in my favour. Ostensibly she was 'worried about me', and my monosyllabic answers perhaps confirmed to her that

I was in need of some kind of support. It would have been mildly amusing to observe her fake sincerity, had the signs not been so unfavourable to me. Her 'compassion' was learned from a thin book called, 'how to act like a caring manager'. Perhaps she had only scanned the glossary of facial expressions and empty words but the whole thing was the usual unconvincing act.

My wife was startled and upset when I arrived home, not because she didn't like me, but because the circumstances were rather suspicious.

'She wants to get rid of you', was almost the first thing she said.

I scoffed at the idea. I said, 'She can't just get rid of me. She's got no reason to get rid of me.' Both of these things were true and at the time I had no idea what the Head's actual motivation was. Nor did she, as it turned out. It was the sixteenth of December and a very unmerry Christmas awaited.

There is never a good time for you to discover that your career is disintegrating but the timing in this instance was particularly poor. We'd had an extension added to our house the previous summer, and the fact that it cost more than the original house put us in a financial situation warranting two incomes rather than one. Around the same time our second child, Charlotte, had been born. We both love her dearly but had my wife and I known what awaited us, we might not have been so quick to have another child.

Diane, still on her maternity leave, collected our elder daughter, Grace, from nursery and I added the finishing touches to her newly decorated bedroom so that it would be ready when she got home. My mind was a turbulent mess of thoughts and worries about the future. I had no idea what was going on. As I attached a Disney lampshade my mind strayed to the unpleasantness of my workplace, the contrast almost too much to bear. How my delightful daughter with her simple, innocent tastes could co-exist with tomorrow's hoodlums, barely a decade older than her, was unfathomable. This juxtaposition was set to get worse in the months ahead, causing me to become introspective and deeply concerned. In fact, 'deeply concerned' is much too superficial an expression to use. My life was to be consumed by people who were only interested in causing me harm. I would be swallowed up by an impersonal bureaucratic machine, unbending, intolerant and merciless, which at some future date would spit me out, uncaring of the mangled thing it had produced.

Naturally, Grace and Charlotte understood nothing about my change in circumstances, and Christmas went ahead in our house seemingly as normal. Diane videoed Grace coming down the stairs to discover the dolls' house that Santa had left her in the night. The rest of the day was the usual blizzard of wrapping paper and excitement, but something was missing, for the adults at least. Diane and I felt the strain of course but none of that was transmitted to our children. Confused as I was, I still couldn't believe that my situation was as desperate as it might seem. But I also vacillated between optimism and dread, an emotional conflict that I hoped was played out in the privacy of my head.

Over the years I had become more of an optimist generally, despite all the evidence I had accrued which seemed to indicate that this optimism was unwarranted. This optimism remained, tempered by my extreme worry.

A sober recounting of the events leading up to my unofficial suspension could lead me to only one conclusion, that being that Ms Fennel, the Headteacher, was concerned for my wellbeing, at least in a superficial sense. If there was a chapter in her handbook which dealt with minor incidents that could be escalated for no discernible reason, then I was assuming that she was adhering pretty rigidly to it. She was making a mountain out of a molehill, without really having enough material to construct the latter let alone transform it into the former. The whole thing was both ridiculous and unsettling. It was a process and a way of thinking that I didn't comprehend. I had no experience of doing things in such an unwieldy, confusing manner. That I should not be privy to the real reasons for all that was happening was dispiriting to say the least.

On Christmas day we went through the motions, trying to make the day fun for the children. Little did we know but we would spend the next two years engaged in this sort of well-intentioned deceit. It was simply impossible to relax but, although I knew nothing of this, the Headteacher's machinations were still unformed at this point. I now know that there was no chance of me understanding what she was up to, simply because she did not understand it herself. She had started a process that she didn't know how to complete, following a procedure that presumably she hadn't read or truly comprehended. The whole affair seemed sinister to me but her intent might have been to resolve the problem fairly at the time. I have no idea.

Those who had vetoed Fennel's appointment previously were to have their reluctance amply justified. She didn't have the intelligence to perform the job she had coveted so badly, but sadly a lack of intellect was not necessarily a bar to advancement in the teaching profession. There were other assets which were more highly prized than intelligence, such as dogged adherence to foolish rules and the ability to engender despondency in underlings. Perhaps Fennel intuitively understood that no matter what she tried to do with me she would be (initially) successful – weak unions and compliant governors would see to that – but she made no allowance for the long-term implications that would prove to be more damaging to her than to me. She had no contingency for dealing with staff who fought back…they so rarely did.

Events were now entirely out of my hands and I could only respond to my employer's demands. From now on I was without recourse to any knowledge of the situation and could not take the initiative in any way. Had my employers been benign that would not have been a problem, but that wasn't the case, even if I didn't yet appreciate the extent of their malevolence.

Communication took the form of letters from various people in various departments, many of whom I never met but whose actions would have a profound effect upon my life. These people could make decisions, assumptions and allegations without the need to ask for my opinion as to the veracity of what they said. They were as powerful as I was weak. I was safely out of the way, ignorant, impotent, friendless – just the way they liked it. My only hope was the union… which was, based on my previous dealings with them, scant comfort to me.

You have to be very careful when you consider using words like 'conspiracy' or 'plot' and yet they are hard to avoid in some cases. What are you supposed to call it when you find yourself under intense scrutiny by powerful people you never meet, who seemingly have no obligation to tell you anything about the reasons behind their interest in you? Why didn't any of them want to speak to me? Why didn't they want my side of the story? Did I not deserve the chance to be heard? Had I no rights? It seemed as if I wasn't important, certainly not in terms of being a witness to the events that had brought about this state of affairs. My feelings transcended mere frustration but they are hard to describe exactly because I simply didn't know what I had to be worried about. It was akin to being scared of the unknown.

Was I subject to a conspiracy then? The problem with conspiracies is not that they don't occur but that they frequently get a bad press. Conspiracy theorist have told us that Neil Armstrong landed on Arizona rather than the moon, that Diana was murdered rather than the victim of a car crash, that Kennedy was killed by the FBI, and that Basil Brush is a real fox. Most of these are hard to reconcile with the established facts or common sense, and as a result conspiracies are all viewed as being reprehensible tripe. But it need not be so, of course. Some conspiracies are proven to be such but then become much less interesting and well publicised when the truth is revealed.

With Christmas over, I was invited to attend a meeting on January 8th with the Headteacher. I supposed that, if nothing else, I would at least find out what was happening to me. Prior to attending this meeting, I received a letter which would really set the tone for everything that was to follow. The letter was undated and signed using a felt tip pen, neither of these facts pointing to a great measure of professionalism. In fact, one could rightly be quite dismissive of someone who signs a letter in felt tip but perhaps I should just be flattered that it wasn't a crayon. The letter was from Kate Ryding, who, it would transpire, was instrumental in everything that followed. That she was incompetent worked to my advantage eventually but in the short term she was extremely damaging to my cause, although all of her actions were couched in caring language.

By way of introduction she explained that she was, 'employed as a Senior Quality Assurance Officer within the Quality Assurance Team, of Targeted Services, Children and Young People's Department', which for me instantly conjured up an image of someone who does vital work. Quite how people arrive at such monolithic job titles is beyond me. What purpose do they serve? How can anyone deduce what that person's function is? Or is that the point? Even worse are those job titles that seem to start with an acronym against which some meaningful words have to be allocated. Kate Ryding's job didn't seem to have an acronym but if it had it would have been SQAOQATTSCYPD. I personally would pay money to hear her try to pronounce that, but as it was I never even met her.

Having explained who she was in a manner that actually left me none the wiser, she then went on to explain why she was writing i.e. that she had 'responsibility for managing allegations that are made against people who work with children (in either a paid or unpaid capacity) within the Children and Young People's Department (including schools) of Blackpool Council.' This came as something of a shock to me as, until this moment, I had no idea that I was alleged to have done anything particularly serious. She further explained that her job was to ensure that the correct procedures were followed at each stage of the investigation, words which would prove to be laughable as events unfolded.

I hesitate to use the word 'bombshell' because I have no idea what a bombshell is, but the aforementioned munition is undoubtedly what Kate Ryding was dropping here. She compounded things by telling me that, 'During the course of the investigation the person who will be offering support to you will be Jill Fennel'. That would have been a great comfort to me had it not been for the fact that it was she who began this whole process. How could she offer me support when it was she who had decided that I was to be investigated? The only good thing to have come from this was that I now knew without any doubt that I was on my own. There was no-one fighting my corner. My mind reeled at the impossibility of the situation I was in.

What sort of support could I expect from my persecutor? It was lunacy.

On her letter it was quite clear that the matter in hand was the incident with John, which she termed, 'physical intervention' and labelled with the wrong date.

January 8th came and I made my way to the Head's office having collected my useless union rep. from his room. Following a cursory round of unpleasantries, during which I was introduced to Carol Gee from Human Resources, the four of us got down to business. I had met Carol Gee before when I was disciplined for calling the science advisor a 'fuckwit' during a faculty meeting. I wouldn't have minded so much but he hadn't even been present. I received a written warning at the time for which my union rep. had thanked the Headteacher. Yeah, thanks. The only good thing to come from that incident was listening to Gill Fennel reading a statement written by one of my colleagues present at the meeting. She gathered from this that I had actually referred to him as a 'fucktwit', which is altogether more twee.

The Headteacher's secretary was there also and it was her job to selectively minute what was said at this and subsequent meetings. It became apparent that I really needed someone to take notes on my behalf, but these would rarely have tallied with what was, I suppose, the official version. Fennel spoke in general terms about the incident with John and then told me that I was to be formally suspended for my safety and for that of the pupils. She went on to explain that there was to be no further disciplinary action taken but that I would be referred to Occupational Health where some sort of assessment would be made about my continued suitability to work as a teacher. As usual, observing the old maxim, 'whatever you say, say nothing', I said very little. Like a criminal I was told to hand over my school keys which I duly did. I was then told that I was to have no contact with any member of the school staff other than my union representative.

Fennel also advised me to visit my GP to speak to him about the stress that I was under, which was odd considering it was she who was causing this stress. I knew at once that to follow her advice, which I later discovered came from her handbook on dealing with such matters, rather than any genuine concern on her part, would be deleterious to my cause. They were clearly going for the 'unsound mind' angle and any visit to the doctor with regards to stress would only be giving them extra ammunition (or should that be 'bombshells'?).

Having said all that Fennel made an extraordinary request, asking if I would write reports for my form! I agreed to do this, despite the fact that I wasn't allowed to set foot on school property. Instead, I was to liaise with my union rep. in order to collect a

USB pen with the appropriate software on it. In retrospect I realised what an incredible cheek she had even asking.

The meeting ended. Deflated, I returned to my car, accompanied by my useless union rep. I wasn't sure if he was under instruction to escort me off the premises or genuinely interested in my welfare. His motives and loyalties had always been rather ambiguous – no table thumping firebrand he. We chatted as we walked down to the prep room where I was to collect any belongings I wanted with me. I said my goodbyes to the science teachers and to Polly Summerlee, the Head of Year Seven. The latter gave me a hug and wished me well. Later she would invent evidence that would help me to lose my job. There would be a great deal of duplicity in the coming months and years.

'At least the disciplinary side of it is done', said the useless union rep. I can't remember my reply. 'Gill is just worried about you. She just wants the old Dave back', he added. I seriously doubted this, as she clearly had been no more a fan of the 'old Dave' than she was of the new one. Despite my fears, this view was more optimistic than the one that I'd held previously. Fennel, her intellect stretched to the limit, had decided that I needed help of some sort. Her benevolence was a paper exercise of course, but better that she was thinking that way than simply trying to cast off what, to her, was a troublesome employee.

The drive home provided me with opportunities to reflect upon my position. As the hills of the Trough of Bowland grew nearer, my mood lifted somewhat. Taking stock, I was able to reach the following conclusions: firstly, I was not the subject of any type of disciplinary investigation; therefore, secondly, I still had a job; and thirdly, I had a bit of time off. I would attend the OH appointment and then return to work, but in the meantime there was plenty of DIY to be done in the new extension. My old doubts were temporarily in abeyance. My wife Diane did not view things the same way, however, and I found it hard to convince her that everything would be okay.

A couple of days later I received two letters, both dated January 8th. One reported the minutes of the meeting that I had attended, and it contained several alarming revelations. For a start it contained the phrase, 'due to the quite serious nature of the incidents before Christmas...' Incidents? Plural? Surely this was a typo – correspondence from my employers was always littered with them. Next in bold type it mentioned the allegation against me:

'Incitement to or use of inappropriate physical intervention to anyone at all on the School's premises or whilst engaged on school business'.

This at least corresponded to the other letter from Kate Ryding which had also used the phrase 'physical intervention'. Reassuringly, I read this phrase also: 'A strategy meeting was held yesterday which is procedure, to decide if the matter should be investigated beyond the school procedures. It was decided that it shouldn't but concerns were raised about RY's health.' That, to me, meant that there was no investigation but that Fennel had a superficial concern for my wellbeing. To some extent this tallied with the apparent need for me to see Occupational Health.

It also mentioned that there had been *three* incidents last term of a similar nature but didn't say what these were. For some reason I don't think that this phrase registered with me completely but there certainly hadn't been three incidents of anything. So far, so dubious, but the other letter was a formal statement concerning my suspension. Bearing in mind that my useless union rep. and I both thought that there were no outstanding disciplinary measures taking place, a fact which seemed to be confirmed in the minutes of the meeting, I was shocked to see that I had been suspended, 'following an allegation of potential Gross Misconduct....' That phrase, relating to an allegation (singular), had never previously been used. My mind was reeling with the implications. I was confused and deeply concerned.

At the start I had been sent home because someone was worried about my health. Then I was under investigation for the incident with John. Then another two incidents had appeared but I wasn't under investigation. Now, we were back to just one incident for which I was being investigated. Luckily, the letter also gave me the name and number of someone who would, 'act as link officer and will maintain contact with you and keep you advised of ongoing progress'. Unfortunately, when I rang my 'link officer' she wouldn't tell me anything about what was going on, on the grounds that it related to a young person and was therefore confidential. I think that that was the last I ever heard from her. Contrary to the letter she didn't maintain contact or advise me of 'ongoing progress'. Is there any other type of progress? Stalled progress? The idea that I was going mad transited briefly through my brain.

This was one of many low points. For a time, my situation seemed hopeless. I already felt that reason and sense had been discarded. The grand-sounding strategy meeting had taken place without any apparent need for me to put across my point of view. I wasn't privy to what was happening, despite the fact that it profoundly affected me. The gradual realisation that events were entirely beyond my control was very corrosive of my morale. To realise that people, who for the most part I didn't know, were plotting against me, building a case but not involving me in any type of communication, was depressing in the extreme, particularly as I had no contact with anyone. Looking back, I would assume that this was all deliberate. How could I formulate any type of defence when I didn't know with what I was being accused? I would have stood a better chance of receiving justice had I been arrested. Had that been the case there would have been obligations to charge me in a clear, precise manner and to give me contact with the people I needed to conduct my defence. I would have been required to make a statement. Failure to do these things would surely have made the case against me untenable. However, none of these measures were deemed necessary in my situation – It would become increasingly clear that the natural rules of justice did not apply.

A few days after being suspended I received another letter congratulating me on my progression to the teacher's upper pay spine (a pay rise) for so many years of satisfactory service. It didn't escape my notice that this represented something of a paradox – on one hand I was being suspended for my conduct within school and on the other being paid extra because I was considered to be doing a good job. Not every teacher got this pay rise – most did, admittedly, but it was not actually a formality.

Chapter Five

A new routine

The Occupational Health Department was situated in an unprepossessing office suite in a leisure centre in Blackpool's South Shore Area. I arrived far too early and took myself out for a walk to kill time. The wind could euphemistically be called 'bracing' and carried with it cold salty spray. When I could no longer take the sight of the town's run-down streets, it's badly maintained houses, litter and self-inflicted degradation, I made my way to OH, asking for directions from a reception desk 'manned' by a young woman who had once been one of my pupils. She had definitely been one of the more pleasant characters I had encountered at Collegiate and smiled as we spoke. She'd been in the first year-seven class I had taught, a nice bunch who had yet to lose the enthusiasm for learning that they had brought with them from primary school. By year eight many of them would be sullen malcontents, a minor tragedy that was repeated year after year with depressing certainty. It was during that transitional period that teachers became the enemy and school a prison.

I reported to another reception desk, telling the staff that I had an appointment to see the Occupational Health Nurse Adviser. Oddly, this was termed a 'follow-up appointment', although it was actually my first visit. I began to feel quite sick as I sat waiting, succumbing to some debilitating winter bug, and I worried that if I looked ill I might be deemed, solely on my appearance, to be having a breakdown of some sort. Maybe this was paranoia. Other than that, I was fairly relaxed, knowing that I was fundamentally well. I was sure that I would find myself back at work the following month.

The Occupational Health Nurse Advisor turned out to be nothing of the sort, but I was becoming used to the unending stream of misinformation with which I was being fed. Instead, I saw Doctor Watson, a man of roughly my age. We chatted for a while, discovering that we had both served in the armed forces, he in the RAF and I in the army. I wondered if these pleasantries simply disguised the fact that the interview had started, so I was wary, striving not to appear like a dangerous lunatic.

Soon he broached the subject of what had brought me there and I recalled the events of December when I had tried to keep John in detention. I explained that I wasn't too sure what was going on and he confessed that he wasn't either.

All-in-all I found him to be a sympathetic character but later worried that this was merely a front he presented to draw some sort of confession from his victims – paranoia again. Doctor Watson told me that he felt that I should return to work. He said that I should have a 'phased return' and that he would ask for more classroom support to help me with unruly pupils, warning that he didn't believe that I would actually get this.

That was that. Back to work. I hadn't done too badly out of it, I supposed. I'd managed to get plenty of work done on the house and I had started to lose a bit of my excess weight through running more miles per week than I could normally manage. Running gave me time to think but my mind was a torrent of possibilities, not all of them pleasant or welcome as I pounded past an increasingly familiar procession of landmarks. As I reached the sign marking the limits of the village I knew that I'd run a mile, and when I got to the disused Cold War bunker, that was one-and-a-third miles. A particular house was two miles and the flyover was two-and-a-half miles. At that point I usually turned back, but sometimes I completed a run which I knew was 6.2 miles in total. On one occasion I ran only one mile, having tripped on my shoelace and gone to ground with the elegance of a felled bison. I didn't sprawl or dive, I just described an angle of ninety degrees straight into the tarmac. My knees took the bulk of the impact and I walked home, hoping that someone

I knew would stop and give me a lift. No one did. Was I disheartened? Very.

Despite my extended holiday, it was hard not to be dismayed at having to go back to that school, absence very definitely not having made the heart grow fonder. Phased return or not, I would still be back in the cauldron of impossible choices, dealing with children who hated me as a matter of course, who could start an argument on any given subject and on a whim. All teachers think about doing something else, some other career, never more so than when they have had a break from it. I'd had six weeks. My classes would be in disarray... but what else was new?

I heard nothing more for some time and settled back into some sort of routine once more, always waiting for a phone call or a letter. By this time my wife had returned to work and we had found a childminder for Charlotte, our younger daughter, because I was due to return to my job at any moment. I filled my days with running and DIY, dropping Grace off at nursery and then picking her up in the afternoon. Aged only three, she didn't twig that it was very odd that her daddy didn't go to work any longer. I couldn't claim to feeling relaxed at this time. I knew that going back was for the best but that didn't make it any more appealing for me.

I was still on full pay and had plenty of useful jobs to be doing. We had bought a new kitchen so I spent time fitting that. I fitted book cases, stripped wall paper, cleaned, tidied... but at the back of my mind always was the thought that my job was waiting for me to return.

February, my least favourite month, passed with no sign of that return. March then became the obvious favourite but for weeks there was still no word. I wondered what the delay could possibly be but pragmatically made use of the time off. I had also by this time completed my form reports in a manner which would provide an amusing aside to the story. Banned from school, I made contact with my useless union rep to collect the USB pen. He arranged for us to meet in the car park of an Indian restaurant which he deemed to be at the midway point between his house and mine. Like a drug dealer and his customer, we carried out our clandestine business under cover of darkness, two furtive figures meeting, exchanging and then parting. The item itself resembled a football or Mickey Mouse or something equally innocuous, ruining the espionage image somewhat but for a brief moment we got to be Cold War spies handing over a roll of microfilm. A few days later I dropped off a coded message in a dead letter box for my contact and we repeated the process. Actually, I rang him but you get the idea. I returned the USB pen and we parted again.

Ridiculous. Had I known what lay ahead, I wouldn't have bothered.

March for me is the start of spring. I used to enjoy putting the date on the board once it got to March, anticipating the spring weather, the brighter days. There would be bank holidays, days out and then the long summer holiday. This March would be different, however. *This March I got the letter.*

The letter shook me to my core – it changed everything. My perspective altered and my confidence dipped alarmingly. What had been merely confusing with a sinister undercurrent now became menacing. The tone of the letter and the words used haunt me even now. I wondered not who I was but who I was perceived to be. It started well enough, 'Dear David' – nothing wrong with that. But then:

Investigation under the Disciplinary Procedure

Details have been received of allegations that you have caused concern by:

Physical or indecent assault on any person whilst engaged, or purporting to be engaged on Trust business, of which there are three separate counts.

The letter was from Gill Fennel, the Headteacher who now described herself as 'Investigating Officer'. Could I take it that she was no longer the person who would be 'offering me support' as had been claimed in a previous letter? Could she be both my persecutor and my confidante? It seemed to stretch credibility somewhat, even by the standards of Blackpool Borough Council. Most alarming of all was the use of the phrase, 'Physical or indecent assault'. My mind reeled with the possibilities.

And then there was the 'three separate counts'. What were these? No one had told me. I knew about the incident with John and it had sparked off this process but there certainly weren't any other instances. The only other thing that they could have been thinking about was the incident with Debbie but I had been exonerated of any blame. I had a letter which included that very word: 'exonerated'.

This was my lowest ebb. Someone thought me capable of indecent assault. If there was a worse accusation that could be made against me then I couldn't think what it was. A murderer would go to jail for longer but there were occasions where a murderer wasn't too badly thought of – crimes of passion and so on – someone who indecently assaulted children, on the other hand...

Still there were no details of my alleged crimes. It struck me then that if I was accused of assault then why weren't the police involved? I assumed that this was a serious charge, requiring their attention.

When I showed the letter to my wife the blood drained from her face. I was now in trouble on a different scale. That night I looked in on Grace as she slept in her bed and wondered what she would have thought if she had known or been able to understand what the man she called Daddy was accused of. I had never felt more wretched.

The next meeting was scheduled for March 31st which meant that I had a week in which to fret. The problem was not that I had done anything wrong but that someone said I had. Increasingly, it seemed that that was enough, as if the accusation were proof in itself. Try as I might, I couldn't think of three things that could be construed as assaults of any kind, let alone indecent assault. The phrase never fails to make me shudder, even now.

This meeting involved me, my useless union rep, Gill Fennel, her secretary, and the ubiquitous Carol Gee. We sat in the memorial room under the gaze of various notables from the school's past, captured in oils or camera film. It was wood-panelled and rather grand, not at all in keeping with the rest of the school which was a masterpiece of concrete, brick and Formica. As usual I said very little, at least to start with, but finally they spelled out the crimes for which I stood accused. Although she never said as much I think that this was the meeting at which I was to offer my resignation, but to me that would have seemed like an admission of guilt and so it was never a viable solution for me.   The three allegations were these: the alleged assault on Debbie in September, another alleged assault on a year seven boy called Jim (not his real name) and the alleged assault on John. The last two had both occurred in December. Finally, after three and a half months I was told what I had actually, allegedly, done wrong. The pretence that there was no investigation was long gone, as was the notion that my wellbeing was the matter in question. At some point things had escalated to this extent and yet if I was *really* believed to have assaulted three pupils why were the police not involved? There were so many incongruities that the case against me seemed laughable.

I challenged Fennel, firstly about the incident with Debbie, saying that I had been exonerated of blame so how could I be investigated for a second time? She didn't really have an answer, obviously having hoped that I would just acquiesce and agree to whatever solution she had in mind. Secondly, I asked her about the witnesses she had to the second alleged assault. Her answer was that it had been reported by the pupil and that my old friend Mrs Summerlee had taken a statement from him. I had never been asked for my version of events and until that moment I had actually forgotten about any involvement with the boy. Thirdly, I stated plainly that in the last instance the only assault was that committed against me. I asked her if that had been investigated.

'We weren't looking at it that way at the time', she said. *No, I bet you weren't*, I thought bitterly. It was this skewed way of dealing with things that had led to these sorts of problems for me and other teachers. Children could say what they liked, knowing that the teacher would be hauled over the coals, regardless of the truth. I actually used that phrase, 'hauled over the coals' and Fennel looked very hurt, assuring me with unintentional irony, that no such thing was happening.

Fennel was almost speechless, deeply discomfited by the fact that I had stood up to her, for no one ever did. Events had plainly not gone as she had planned. In my fragile mental state, I should have broken under the strain and the weight of 'evidence' against me. I should have been crushed by the amassed charges arrayed but I was in no mood to roll over. Angrily, I asked which of these incidents was considered to be an 'indecent assault?' Fennel replied that it was merely a phrase from a stock letter and didn't mean that any such accusation actually existed; scant comfort after the hellish week I had just endured thinking that someone had accused me of such a thing.

Having warmed to my subject, I told the Head that the behaviour in the school was hopeless and that discipline was breaking down to such an extent that it was becoming impossible to teach. Naturally, she denied that this was so and said that most staff were quite happy with the situation. I wondered who she had been talking to. I was bloody sure I couldn't find anyone who thought that way but maybe that's what teachers told her when asked. My colleagues were almost universally poor at speaking out, but an anonymous survey carried out some months later was to confirm what I had said.

Furthermore, she informed me that both she and Carol Gee had looked at the Doctor's report on me and that they considered it to be 'inconclusive'. If he had written what he said he was going to write (and much later I found out that he had), then his report was not inconclusive at all; far from it, in fact. He had reached a conclusion, that being that I should return to work. What she meant was that his report had not reached the conclusion that they had wanted i.e. that I was a threat to children.

They also mentioned that I hadn't discussed all three incidents with him to which I responded by reminding them that today was the first time I had actually been told what they were! Clearly, they now had an inkling that they had mishandled the situation, it was plain from their faces. I hoped that they might give up.

Wearily, Fennel said that the matter of the assault on Jim would be reinvestigated and the meeting ended with Fennel looking ashen-faced and worried. It was a satisfactory result for me. My useless union rep, whose loyalties I had always privately questioned, was gloating on my behalf.

'I shouldn't say this but I do enjoy seeing people squirm', he said. In a sense he was right – I had definitely won that round and the initiative was mine. Later, as I sat in a café with Diane, I found myself quite relaxed, triumphant even. I had put the record straight, said my piece and given Fennel and Gee nowhere to go, and what's more, they both knew it.

The trick would have been for it to stay that way but again I found myself isolated as the plot against me changed course without my knowledge. At least Fennel knew that I couldn't be railroaded but that merely made her more determined to find something substantial to use against me. In the coming months I would discover that what anyone said against me would be taken as the gospel truth and anything that I said about myself would be considered to be a lie. A lack of evidence was no barrier to engineering my downfall. I think that having been suspended for such a long time they felt that nothing less than my dismissal would suffice when it came to justification for this prolonged absence during which they had had to pay for a supply teacher to cover my lessons. It was becoming imperative that I was found guilty of *something* and henceforward the matter was investigated with a view to finding me guilty rather than establishing the facts.

I could only sit back, isolated and ignorant, as a case was built against me. I was entirely passive.

There was no response I could make, no enquiries, no witnesses for the defence to be found, no representative thinking of ways to undo the damage. I still had not been asked to make statements about the second two alleged incidents, nor was there any suggestion that to do so might be useful in presenting a balanced argument at whatever sort of trial awaited me.

In the coming weeks the initiative slipped away from me like a man swimming for the river bank only to be swept away at the last moment as he grasped for a tree root. I was left with my thoughts. I ran through each incident again and again, convinced that there could be no case against me even if all the allegations were taken at face value. In particular I ran through the middle incident, trying to establish how exactly it had come to be considered an assault...

The matter had been dealt with. It was over, finished and everyone was happy with the outcome. It had never been an assault, and no-one had ever said that it was. It had never been investigated and I had never made a statement about it. I knew all this but still I agonised about it, playing the sequence of events over and over in my head, trying to find how it had brought me to this point. If I was thought to have assaulted the boy then why had it taken three and a half months for someone to draw my attention to this fact?

The science department was responsible for break time duties in the dinner hall. Two teachers would stand guard in the canteen and two in the assembly hall, the two divided by a huge folding partition made from wood. Break time in the dinner hall provided us with a pre-death glimpse of hell, as immense queues of children vied with each other to select, pay for and eat some cooked food, all in fifteen minutes. Quite why they needed a cooked meal at this time of the day was unknown; it was literally 'just one of those things'. It was a major logistical challenge, especially given the fact that the multitude had to be fed in such a short time. For the staff it required diplomacy (pleading with children to do as they were told) and the ability to be in two places at once (which should be called 'geographical bi-presence'). We were forbidden from releasing our classes before the bell sounded but those staff on duty had to be there (ideally) before the bell sounded. Something of a challenge.

Over the years a system had evolved in which the children were corralled as they entered the hall by directing them into confined space, thus forcing them to queue. Even then the confined space in question, defined by the only solid wall in the hall and a row of chairs, merely produced a long, thin scrum of hungry humanimals. The atmosphere was one of frenetic forward motion, tension and over-active salivary glands, demonstrating the thin line between acceptable behaviour and savagery. It was another example of a school-made opportunity for conflict between staff and pupils, the former wanting discipline, the latter wanting food.

Each breaktime was a study in discord, a clash of ideology with staff hugely outnumbered and increasingly powerless to impose their will. The welfare staff valiantly held their ground against the swell of partially-formed humanity. They stoically accepted their lot, demonstrating good humour in the face of overwhelming odds but it fell to the two teachers on duty to impose discipline. It was easier to look away than to make a stand but my conscience rarely let me do this. I couldn't abide the rudeness, the queue jumping and the littering. I hated to see the younger pupils being pushed down the queue by older ones, eager for their sausage sandwich. I hated the few, simple, sensible rules being flouted just for the sake of creating a confrontation. Trying to remove a recalcitrant pupil brought with it the near certainty of verbal abuse and an evocation of human rights, often from the pupil's friends who thought nothing of ganging up on a teacher to share their opinions on the matter.

Often, I wondered why I was in this position. As ever I felt isolated, beleaguered and frankly, vulnerable. Events would prove that my fears were not ill-founded.

I can barely remember the boy's name so I won't even try. Even if I remembered it I would still give him a fictitious moniker for the purposes of this book. He was in year seven, one of the new breed who considered themselves to be above the rules. He was allowed, as far as he was concerned, to say and do what he liked, a concept which he amply demonstrated when I asked him to leave the hall having pushed into the queue. He refused. I can see why companies tend to ignore your first letter of complaint regarding faulty goods or services – the culture of let's ignore the problem and see if it goes away. It was the same tactic routinely employed by this young man and many others like him. Presumably it worked some of the time but it didn't quite fit with my old-fashioned ethos of children doing what they are told by the adults in charge of them. Perhaps I wasn't being child-centric enough. As ever, out of step with the times. It was certainly the case that a growing number of our pupils viewed such demands from staff as unreasonable.

His wrongdoing could effectively be transferred to the person who attempted to deal with it, making them the transgressors by means of voluble complaint. After a brief argument in which I was instructed to 'fuck off', he did leave the hall, escorted by me. I was seething by the time I returned to my station. I could complain about his conduct, of course, just as long as I was prepared to explain what I had done to provoke him... thus, it was hardly worth the effort. More and more we were expected to turn a deaf ear, despite the fact that this is a recipe for encouraging similar behaviour. Little did I know but the 'straw that broke the camel's back' was on its way. My 'assault' upon Jim was imminent.

I was next to the welfare lady, near the head of the queue/throng as it pulsated towards the hot food counter like a malevolent human snake. From this vantage point I could intervene when the queue got out of hand whilst still *keeping watch on the rest of the hall, itself a heaving mass of young people in various stages in their own personal feeding frenzy. Feeling a tap on my shoulder I spun round, assuming that I was being subjected to the sort of casual teacher baiting that was proliferating in school. You know the trick – tap someone on their right shoulder but stand behind their left or vice versa. The culprit was Jim, the little year seven boy who unwittingly became used as an instrument in my downfall and I tore a strip a metaphorical (not actual) strip off him, demanding to know why he had touched me.*

It may sound like an over-reaction on my part and I later recognised it as such. He wasn't a bad lad by any means, quite the reverse, in fact. Not long out of primary school, he probably thought nothing of making physical contact with his teacher as he had done with me. The fact remains that he shouldn't have done it but it was an innocent gesture and my reaction was disproportionate to his minor wrongdoing. I told him that he was to remain where he was and that he would be seeing his head of year (Polly Summerlee) when break was finished. He looked very upset. Apparently, he had merely wanted to know if he was in my lesson next – he was. By the time the bell went I had calmed down somewhat but the boy followed me to Polly's office which was on the way to my room.

She wasn't there so we made our way to the lesson. The lesson itself was the usual disaster, involving a practical experiment which went wrong and after which some of the

85

children refused to tidy up. Such obdurate behaviour, especially from the school's youngest pupils, was still a shock to me. The following week in the same lesson one boy pushed his mate into me and laughed in my face when I challenged him about doing so. I was supposed to put up with it.

After our chaotic hour together had passed, the bell sounded to signal lunchtime for year seven; a second ecstasy of consumption so soon after the first. I let Jim go to get his food. I didn't give our little contretemps much thought until the following morning.

I took my usual long walk down from the staff room to my lab at the furthest end of the school. It was so far off the beaten track that I'm surprised any pupils ever joined me there. Frankly, it would have been easier if they hadn't bothered but implicit in the teacher's role is the presence of pupils. I was awake but fatigued, my morale battered, my soul bruised, but this was my normal state. Like most teachers, my day-to-day existence was just a series of actions rather than 'life'. We lived for the holidays, more or less writing off the other, larger portion of our lives. Those who criticise teachers for their long and frequent holidays are usually the first to admit that they would not want to do their job, seemingly unaware of the irony. The stress of teaching in British schools makes the holidays vital for survival.

Polly was seated at her desk as I passed. We generally exchanged some sort of grim greeting in the morning, both too tired for anything remotely joyous. This morning there was a slight variation on the theme.

'Dave I've been told about an incident with Jim ********', she said. I came into the office and stood. I knew immediately what she was talking about.

'Yeah, I know. I over-reacted a bit', I answered. Her explanation of the event developed no further.

'It was his birthday'. I cringed as she told me this. Being bellowed at by a teacher wasn't exactly what you wanted on your birthday. I felt really sorry for the boy – wrong place, wrong time.

'Right Polly. I'll find him and say sorry. I'll let you know what happens.' Polly agreed to that. There was nothing in her manner to indicate that we were talking about a particularly serious issue. Later however she quoted me as having said, 'Oh my God', a blasphemous phrase, which despite my personal lack of religious beliefs I rarely use for fear of causing offence.

That, in essence, was our conversation. During the day I found Jack, apologised, and gave him a pound coin to get something from the canteen at break. The last action may have been ill-advised and indeed it would subsequently be portrayed as a bribe to gain the boy's silence, but I found Polly later in the day and told her what I had done. She seemed pleased with the efforts I had made to sort things out and she knew that, as always, I had the children's best interests at heart. On many occasions previously, she had

praised me for my care and compassion as a form tutor. She
knew that I was the type of teacher who did his best and
she said as much during my disciplinary meeting, whilst
incongruously giving evidence about my violent conduct
towards this boy.

At the meeting of the 31st of March, the one in which the charges were finally laid in front of me, this incident had somehow escalated into an assault. Apparently, the boy had accused me of grabbing hold of him and pinning him against the wall. He had made a statement to Polly about this but no mention of it had been made to me. Fennel had produced a copy of the statement and a letter from the boy's parent, in which she did indeed allude to an incident of some sort but also expressed her satisfaction with how I had dealt with the matter.

I put it to Fennel that it was odd that she was so ready to express her gratitude to me when I had allegedly assaulted her son. She was confused. I also asked her where her witnesses were. Despite having several hundred possible witnesses to the alleged assault she couldn't actually find one from the staff or pupils. I asked her how, when neither the boy nor I had been standing near a wall and the nearest wall was probably five metres away, shielded by a queue of pupils and a line of chairs, I had managed so effortlessly to pin him against it. I had done this with no one seeing me and without disturbing any of the normally vociferous children in the process.

She had no answers to any of this but said that the matter would be investigated. The investigation that followed consisted of asking the boy to repeat his original statement. No witnesses were ever sought, and I was still not asked to make a statement. The boy's next statement differed in detail but the fact that he had made more than one statement was used as evidence that he was telling the truth and that I was lying.

I am fairly confident that had I been in police custody at this point, accused of the same, that my solicitor would be strongly advising that I be released and the case dropped for a lack of evidence. During the meeting I had helpfully summarised the case against me for Fennel, recognising that she was clearly confused. I had been suspended for three acts of assault. The first of these had been investigated and I had been exonerated of any blame. The second consisted of an alleged assault in front of hundreds of people, not one of whom had seen it, and involved me picking a boy up and transporting him five metres to pin him against a wall by either his bag strap or the back of his collar, depending on which conflicting account you chose to believe. The third assault was actually carried out against me but as she herself admitted they 'weren't looking at it like that the time'. Fennel was flummoxed but she would regroup in the weeks to come.

Ten days later a copy of the minutes was delivered. The minutes always arrived late and I began to wonder if this was done to make my recollection of the events of the meetings hazy. There was no reason why I shouldn't have received them within two or three days. I can never prove it but there would be a series of peculiar events that a suspicious person might view as subterfuge. This may have been part of the pattern or just plain incompetence; there was plenty of the latter.

Naturally, the minutes were not quite an accurate reflection of what was said. In a letter of my own I explained what was missing, including Fennel's comment about not looking into the assault upon me. The minutes came back to me in amended form with this section still missing at which point I realised that they would only ever say what Fennel intended them to say. Things that reflected badly on her i.e. that she was not prepared to investigate an assault upon one of her staff with the alacrity that she used to investigate a so-called assault by a member of staff upon a pupil, were simply omitted. There was simply nothing that I could do to ensure that the minutes were accurate. How could I prove what was said?

While I waited for my next OH appointment I concentrated on my running. I had made a conscious decision to lose weight, and by April I had lost about a stone. I had also reached the point where I was weighing my food and trying to avoid all the things that I actually enjoyed eating. I went to bed starving every night. When I eventually was free to make contact with any of my old friends and colleagues, they commented that I looked gaunt, assuming that my weight loss was due to the stress of my situation. Talking of these colleagues it came as a considerable shock to me to find that no-one was ever told where I had gone or why. Perhaps they didn't care, either. I wasn't everyone's cup of tea. Two other teachers had also gone around the same time, one for persistent absence and another for allegedly having a lesbian affair with a pupil. Perhaps their demise took the edge off mine.

The residual satisfaction from the meeting of 31st March began to dwindle as time wore on. No news was *never* good news, in my case. The plot against me (that word again) was developing in ways which I would not find out about until much later.

I was requested to get a report from my GP about my prior use of the drug Fluoxetine, which had been prescribed for me to help with depression. I thought that this was a rather intrusive request and that it was also irrelevant, but I complied, making sure that Blackpool Borough Council picked up the bill. Still I refused to go back on that drug. I knew that I would be damned for not using it when I was clearly a deranged madman in need of medication. I also knew that I would be damned *for* using it for largely the same reasons; I was mad so I needed my medicine and had acted so violently in the past because I hadn't taken it. It was Catch 22. The fact that I was being treated for depression which does not manifest itself in aggression was not important; it didn't fit with the pattern they were trying to establish so they would make it fit. Once again this was not to be an isolated occurrence.

My next visit to OH followed much the same pattern as the last one, even in so far as seeing the same doctor. As before we chatted and as before I wondered if this seeming preamble was in fact the start of the official assessment. I thought it unlikely that Dr Watson would arrive at a very different verdict from the last attempt, not least because to do so would be to undermine his own judgement. He did ask why I hadn't mentioned all three incidents to him and was satisfied when I explained that I myself had not been apprised of these at the time. Furthermore, he tacitly agreed with me when I suggested that something sinister was afoot. I remember the sage nod of his head and realised that he was a man acquainted with such double dealing.

His recommendation was that I should return to work and much later the very people who had asked for his services would be rather dismissive of his judgement. Again, he simply didn't say what Fennel and Gee wanted him to say. The poor things couldn't get him to see that I was, in fact, a dangerous lunatic. It must have been very frustrating for them, but in the end it made no difference. The fact that it was he who was qualified to make a judgement on my suitability to be a teacher and had been requested by them on two occasions to do so made no difference, they simply cast aside his expertise when it didn't suit their overall plan. Had I known this I might have acted differently but when I ran through the case against me, as I did every day, I just couldn't believe that I could come to any harm. On my runs I summarised the situation: exonerated, no witnesses, assault upon me and the doctor says I should return to work. It wasn't quite a mantra because I considered it in more detail than that, but these were unassailable facts.

During this period, I heard virtually nothing from my union. I assume that my useless union rep was still living in the belief that Fennel just 'wanted to see the old Dave back', whereas things had clearly moved on since that point and he just hadn't kept pace with developments. Following one meeting, I forget which, he told me that he was in a difficult situation because he, in effect 'wore three hats'. He was fond of hat-related symbolism. His first hat, he explained, was his concern for the school, his second might have been for me as a friend and his third was his role as useless union rep. I didn't say anything, ever loath to alienate the one ally I had, but I thought that his three-hat assertion was ridiculous; he had one responsibility when acting as useless union rep

– to his fellow union member. When I was disciplined previously for my scurrilous verbal attack on the science advisor I got the impression that my useless tri-hatted union rep was one of those who 'told on me'. He was certainly anxious not to represent me at the subsequent disciplinary meeting.

My children were unaware of the drama. Charlotte was still a baby, less than a year old, and Grace was only three. For Diane it was a different story. She knew (better than I did as it transpired) exactly what I was up against. Only once did she ask what had happened – just checking that I was the innocent man she thought I was. Again, the only phrase that fits is 'no smoke without fire'. She had a heightened sensitivity to the possibility of 'talk'. Whether or not any of her colleagues were engaged in idle gossip, it must have felt as if they were. Neither of us really derived much enjoyment from life for the next two years, our happiness, in effect, stolen from us. We were never fully able to enjoy Charlotte's early years or Grace starting school because this menacing event was in the background, leaving us unsettled and despairing. It wasn't just the fact that my job or my career was at risk but that my good name lay in the hands of people who didn't care what they did to me.

Chapter Six

Help wanted

My next meeting with Fennel and her bunch of chums was scheduled for 9th of June. At some point I decided that I needed greater support than I was currently receiving i.e. almost none. I had spoken to someone at the Citizens Advice Bureau, but my visit yielded no results at all. Next I spoke to a solicitor. I gave him the facts but I had the clear feeling that this was something out of his range of expertise. He asked why I wasn't using the union and I explained about their *laissez faire* attitude.

Perhaps he took this as an indication that my version of events didn't quite reflect reality. After all, if what I claimed was true then they would be chomping at the bit, fighting to save the reputation of their colleague. It was a free consultation but he said that if I wanted he would write a letter to the school, complaining about the length of time it was taking. Instead, I reported my visit to the useless union rep who at once told me that I should be using a NUT solicitor! At last I felt that things were moving in the right direction but why did it take my visit to a solicitor to precipitate this action? Had it not been obvious before that someone with expertise in the field of educational law was required?

The next investigation meeting was scheduled for 8th of June and this time I had a union case worker with me. My rep was called Martin Fisher and I met with him briefly before the meeting to discuss our strategy. Mr Fisher – and I never called him anything else – was a rather distinctive figure who wore a fedora and a long mac, rather in the fashion of a gangster. This belied his gentle nature, although he did prove to have a certain tenacity in his dealings with the school authorities.

He began by establishing that this meeting was for investigatory purposes, which it was. He then clarified the exact nature of the complaints against me and they were indeed as previously mentioned. He asked me about the incident with Jim, which now seemed to be pivotal to the school's case, in particular about whether or not I had grabbed him. I said that I hadn't. He asked if I had pushed the boy against the wall and again I replied that I hadn't. It carried on in that form for a few minutes, my version of events being laid out in plain terms. It became apparent that the incident with Jim had not been investigated because, they said, I had admitted to it.

This became a major stumbling block and it was clearly my word against that of Polly Summerlee, who was speaking for the boy in question. It was a question of who was to be believed. I stated that Polly and I had never had a conversation about any alleged assault and I had admitted to nothing of the sort. She said that I had. Ironically, in view of the harm her 'mistakenness' would do to my credibility she claimed that she hadn't reported the matter to anyone else out of friendship. Her subsequent investigation into the matter had involved her asking the boy to recount the events once again. What were the chances of him now saying that he had elaborated upon the actual events? Was he likely to admit to having lied about what had actually occurred? Was he even questioned with a view to allowing the possibility of a lie?

The boy could not be cross-examined in a hearing simply because he was a child, and so his evidence stood as a gospel account of the events of that morning. The fact that no witnesses could be found was apparently due to fact that it had taken place so long ago and that any witnesses couldn't be relied upon to remember the events clearly. Ms Fennel even stated that she couldn't question the welfare staff about the incident because she didn't know who had been on duty, although I am quite sure she would have a list with this information on it. Even still, they were not huge in number and could have been gathered together to ask if any of them had seen anything; the assault that was described to me would have been a memorable event had it occurred.

The only witness that could be called was Matthew Dodd, who was on duty in the hall at the same time. He was called to the formal disciplinary hearing convened on 3rd July.

The letter which informed me of this meeting stated that I would be required to respond to the following allegation:

Incitement to or use of inappropriate physical intervention to anyone at all on the School's premises or whilst on school business.

The random use of capital letters and the lack of punctuation is down to the school, not me. I'd heard this allegation before. On the surface of it, it was a less serious charge than one of 'physical or indecent assault'. They seemed to be shying away from that now as if they had made a mistake. I didn't want the phrase discarded so readily. The implication was simply too great for me to forgive them and I questioned its use at every opportunity. This most recent letter had also dispensed with the informal, 'Dear David' greeting. It was now, 'Dear Mr Roy'; easier to sack someone with no first name.

The next bombshell (what *is* a bombshell?) came in a report which I received a few days later. I scanned the report but almost missed this crucial sentence and the important between-the-lines information it contained, but luckily Martin Fisher spotted it.

'Given the nature of all three incidents in a relatively short period of time it is my recommendation that Mr Roy should be dismissed.'

Finally, there it was: confirmation of the twisted logic that was driving this whole process along. At some point the idea of getting 'the old Dave back' had been superseded by one which was basically, 'let's make sure that the old Dave never comes back.' Events had see-sawed so dramatically that it wasn't always clear what the school's ultimate aim was. It was clear now. The doctor's reports counted for nothing. The lack of evidence counted for nothing. It wasn't even the children involved in these incidents or their parents that were pushing for this action, it was the Headteacher, Gill Fennel and her cabal of HR cronies.

So, there it was. She was really saying that I was guilty, and Martin Fisher presented a grim picture for me. Every other point of the report could be countered, discussed, argued, disputed, but that bold statement stood out as a magnificently negative testimonial. When the Headteacher, that supreme arbiter of right and wrong, that expert in education and children, that profound caring, all-powerful being who sat at the helm of the ship each day, calmly steering a course to universal enlightenment – when they said you had to go, who would argue?

Martin knew this. He had vast experience of these matters. The governors, after a sham trial in which all the evidence was presented and discussed, would side with the Head. That's how it was, as night followed day. It was an unalterable tenet, as if the governors had unshakable belief in this one flawless person. Martin's view was upheld by a friend of mine who had been the senior technician at the school and a long serving governor. She told me that only once had the governors ever actually challenged one of the Head's ideas. 'Oh dear, David', she said when I told her.

The report, the basis for the subsequent 'hearing', laid out the facts according to Gill Fennel. It contained reference to the various statements made by staff and by pupils. It stated that despite the fact I disputed the veracity of some of the evidence, the events *had* occurred as recounted by the witnesses. It was all very damning simply because it was designed that way. Fennel had sewed me up well and truly and, although I couldn't quite believe it could possibly lead to my dismissal, it was, in fact, a foregone conclusion.

As usual the big event was held in the grand surroundings of the Memorial Room, the wise patrons of yesteryear looking down on a contemporary fallen angel. I imagined their mute displeasure as the 'facts' were set out.

My jury was a panel of governors. One was deputy chair of governors and it was he who presided over the 'trial'. On one side of him he had a parent governor and on the other the head of the neighbouring sixth form college which had once been part of the school. The composition of these panels has often been described as incestuous i.e. drawn from people who, if not actually related to the Headteacher, or each other, might as well be. The chances of the deputy chair of governors and the head of a neighbouring establishment siding with me against Fennel were beyond remote; only the parent governor offered some hope but could only ever be in the minority.

Martin pointed out to me that Fennel was almost certainly on the governing body of the college, so a nice reciprocal arrangement was no doubt in place whereby the respective headteachers could metaphorically scratch each other's backs. Justice be damned. I wasn't being judged by 'twelve good men and true' nor was there any pretence that this was the case.

As before, I could actually see the benefits of being in court charged with a criminal offence. Why wasn't I? Do three allegations of physical or indecent assault against children not constitute something that should be in the realm of the Ministry of Justice?

Surely a vicious, violent child-molester should be investigated fully? Rather than a jury of people with no preconceived ideas and no fixed loyalties, I had to contend with a panel of people who were no better than friends of the headteacher.

The problem was that this – this sham trial – was all I had. This was my chance to explain what had happened but having done so I could only hope for the best. I had, through Martin Fisher, to make the right impression and hope that some vestige of justice could be dragged from the unpromising collection of circumstances arrayed before me. A surprising calm settled on me as I took my seat. I was present but passive, the responsibility delegated to Martin. Despite that, much of what occurred is now something of a blank to me and I am forced to refer to the minutes of the meeting to formulate any sort of account at all.

These minutes were to play their own role in the story at a much later date. Due to the usual mix of malice and incompetence I never received a copy of them and even at the next stage in the process, my appeal, Martin and I found ourselves to be the only people present not in possession of these minutes. Furthermore, the reasoning laid out for my dismissal was deemed at tribunal to not even match the criteria selected for dismissing me, as if they had missed the point really... but all of that lay in the future.

Our complement was strengthened by the presence of yet another HR bod, Richard Darby. I was eventually to be very grateful for his presence for his easy-going nature disguised a deep grain of incompetence that would prove very useful at Tribunal. I wasn't thinking that far ahead yet but Martin and I had discussed what we were going to do at Appeal, a measure of his confidence in the procedure I was going through. Martin's primary contention was that the first case against me should never have been dragged up again because I had been exonerated of blame. The other side's response was that it could because it formed part of a pattern of events, presumably violent, against children. Quite how exoneration could be deemed part of this pattern was never explored. The finding of the investigation was that I hadn't behaved inappropriately so what was the link between that and alleged incidents of assault? This spurious logic stuck and there would be no shift from my persecutors. Martin further mentioned the fact that Fennel was a JP (God help us all) and that she surely could see that I was being tried for the same crime twice. This obvious, unavoidable fact fell on deaf ears, but I did take some comfort from the fact that the governors did appear to be paying a great deal of interest to the evidence. Maybe things weren't so hopeless after all...

The phrase they revisited time and again was 'safeguarding'. *Safeguarding legislation, safeguarding measures*, these were things drawn up to protect children from abuse, and quite rightly so. The relatively isolated but high-profile failings of the system when it came to individual children in the care of unscrupulous adults, had made it necessary to tighten things up. No-one would ever want a repeat of the situation with Ian Huntley at Soham, where he had managed to kill Jessica Chapman and Holly Wells despite being in a position of trust that involved him being around children, but as ever this legislation had become a catch-all, sometimes used inappropriately by lay people with inadequate training or sense.

The problem with legislation designed to right a wrong is that those who bring it about sometimes don't know when to stop, which leads to the maddening culture of political correctness that afflicts the country. We have measures to prevent people being insulted by things that the people in question had never even thought of as an insult until the idea had been suggested to them, and so it was with safeguarding. Safeguarding could be used as a justification to hound a man out of his job, destroy his career and ruin his good name. No smoke without fire, he must have done something, better safe than sorry...

The hastily collected evidence contradicted itself so often that we got bogged down in an examination of minutiae. It was all to no avail. It didn't matter if no one involved could give a reasonable, measured account of what had gone on. It didn't matter that no one had ever asked me what I thought had gone on. It didn't matter that no one had witnessed anything that could be considered an assault. It was safeguarding. I began to sense that things were not running in my favour.

From the meeting of March when I had amply demonstrated that the case was a crock, the initiative and impetus had completely changed hands. This, my dismissal, was going to go through regardless. I took time to study the faces of the governors. The deputy chair who headed my little jury and who was the *de facto* judge, was inscrutable insofar as his face was as devoid of apparent intelligence as ever. The prim Headteacher of the college was very thorough in her note-taking, a consummate professional very much as Fennel saw herself. I had no great faith in her.

The parent governor seemed my best bet and I like to think that she saw the 'trial' for what it was. I thought of their backgrounds to see if that offered me any hope. I had taught Mr Neath's two children, one more successfully than the other. I thought that I had probably taught the other governor's son and he and I had got along well. Did this count for anything? I thought of the times when I had listened to Mr Neath's interminable descriptions of the latest budgie fancying event he had been too, feigning interest and even asking what I thought might be pertinent questions though I scarcely cared for or listened to the answers. Mr Neath was perhaps something of a dodderer, not in possession of rapier sharp intellect. Had he found in my favour, of course, I would be saying how his down to earth manner belied his immense wisdom and penetrating insight into the world of education, of how he was an intellectual giant clothed in the unassuming uniform of the working man. But he didn't.

During the hearing I resisted the temptation to shout out helpful comments like, 'that's a bloody lie' or 'haven't you listened to anything I've said?' not because the appropriate opportunities for such observations didn't arise but because I thought that doing so might jeopardise my chances of receiving justice. I could imagine Fennel saying something like, 'I think this proves that Mr Roy is unstable', followed by a lot of solemn nodding.

In fact, there was no need for me to say anything much except in answer to any questions directed at me. Martin Fisher was my voice and it was probably just as well. Silence could be interpreted as brooding lunacy, talking as excitable lunacy. If the seed of the idea that I was somehow deranged had been planted, then anything I did could be taken as evidence that this was so. I imagined that the more normal I tried to appear the more mad I would make myself look, like a drunk acting as if they are not drunk. That's certainly how it would be if I were the subject of a conspiracy, which I wasn't, of course.

The question I could ask myself is this, 'was there ever any chance of me bringing about a favourable outcome?' Martin had said he would settle for something less than dismissal; a final written warning, for instance. I personally didn't think that I deserved this or any other punishment, but Martin was more pragmatic, realising that this wasn't about anything so elusive and ethereal as justice; this was about saving my job. Was justice within my grasp?

Alternatively, was injustice in which I at least kept my job within my grasp? Or was it simply the case that having been suspended for six months there was no alternative but to push ahead and dismiss me? How could such a long, paid absence be explained or justified?

As my hopes faded I pondered a few other downturns I'd had in my teaching career, realising that each one was attributable to the same person. Once I had been head of biology, a post offered to me by the head of science a number of years previously and grudgingly agreed to by the then headteacher, Mr McGrath, with the words, 'well, make sure you ask everyone else first.' With that ringing endorsement I held the post for five years on a lower rate of pay than any other head of subject until Gill Fennel decided to scrap it altogether.

At the same time, she took away from me the post of After School Club Manager, which I had held for seven or eight years. My pay took a serious hit that year. The following year I took on responsibility for the school's anti-bullying programme in an unpaid capacity which took up a considerable amount of time. I did the job rather well, even if I do say so myself, and asked for nothing in return. My reward? Fennel asked me to apply for the post, tantamount to saying we want someone else to do it. I didn't apply and amusingly, nor did anyone else. By the time she had done this I had sorted out countless bullying issues and nearly, with a great deal of expert help, completed a computerised reporting system so that the situation could be monitored closely.

Martin had definitely shied away from including these previous career problems in my defence, saying rightly that I would be unable to prove that my latest troubles were part of an ongoing vendetta. For me, it was hard to escape the conclusion that it was though. Sacking me could be viewed as the ultimate expression of the Headteacher's disdain for me and my teaching.

I was an old-fashioned teacher at a time when you had to be modern and forward thinking. I insisted upon good behaviour from the pupils in my class and was quite unbending in that respect, rarely negotiating as Fennel thought I should. If anything, her ethos harked back to the sixties, the era of free love and expression, when anything went and we trusted the essential goodness of the human psyche. Such ideas ignored the truth of human nature and the fact that group behaviour would always sink to the lowest common denominator.

My realisation that this hearing was in fact a done deal was tempered with a thin strand of optimism. Knowing that I had done nothing wrong, and that I could defend my actions, helped enormously. My own personal assessment of the three incidents that had led me to this place indicated that I would prevail despite the fact the 'trial' had tangibly gone against me. I just couldn't accept any other outcome than exoneration, but Martin was pessimistic, his view being along the lines of, 'well we did our best'.

There were aspects of his strategy that I had disagreed with but I had signed an undertaking to agree with the way in which my defence was conducted. To argue with the person assigned to assist made no sense but his assertion that, with help, I could be rehabilitated, stuck in my craw. As far as I was concerned I had done nothing wrong, so the fact that with the aid of medication I could be re-integrated to school life and back to teaching was just plain wrong. I thought that I was being portrayed as a recovering or saveable loon, when I was nothing of the sort. This portrayal I felt actually played into the hands of those whose task it was to dismiss me, but I found out much later that Martin's strategy was simply to cover as many bases as he could when it came to giving reasons *not* to dismiss me.

The fact remained that my defence contradicted itself, as innocence didn't sit well with the possibility of rehabilitation. Either I had done nothing wrong or I had done *something* wrong but could be saved from myself. It was all clouded by my use, or non-use, of fluoxetine, which to me was a total irrelevance but to my detractors was perhaps the key to my alleged violent conduct. I actually thought that it was against the law to consider my use of anti-depressants in this way but they did so regardless; at this stage they could do whatever they wanted, in fact. It would not always be so.

It was clear that the medical opinion they had sought on two occasions was going to be disregarded as unhelpful so they could really get on with the job of crucifixion by some other means. The last thing they wanted was to have someone saying that I was of sound mind and could return to work. From their perspective, Doctor Watson clearly didn't know what he was talking about. How could he have missed my patent lunacy?

It was a very flexible arrangement which suited their purposes well and stifled my chances of getting justice.

There were other things I didn't agree with in my defence, notably Martin's reference to the fact that no witnesses had been sought to the middle incident with Jim. A better argument, I felt, and one which was either closer to the truth or impossible to disprove, was that no witnesses *could be found*. My alleged crime was carried out in the most unfavourable circumstances for the perpetrator, i.e. in front of hundreds of people, but I knew that there were no witnesses simply because the assault hadn't actually happened.

Again, I had to accept his judgement and of course, as I said before, it was a done deal in any case – I just didn't know that. Martin did and he pulled out every mitigating circumstance he could think of. He realised that justice was something that could only be torn forcibly from the grip of the school authorities and not a natural consequence of the disciplinary procedure. Only by clutching at every straw could he hope to save me and yet he remained intractably pessimistic.

If these inconsistencies were my undoing then those of the 'prosecution' were simply ignored. At one point, Fennel had said that there was a mark on John's face, the implication being that I had put it there in what they thought had been a tussle. They weren't bothered about the fact that there was no proof of how he had got that mark and had no medical or police evidence to support the claim.

111

They seemed to want to use it if was going to stick and discard it if it wasn't; it was only evidence if it worked in their favour, in other words – hardly a sound basis for an investigation. The fact that I had restrained the same boy was taken as being an assault, no consideration given to the possibility that I might have been justified in restraining him, following his assault upon me.

The fact that teachers are allowed to restrain pupils in certain circumstances was ignored in favour of Fennel's own personal doctrine, which she herself did not always adhere to, that children should never be restrained under any circumstances. My restraint of the boy simply wasn't a crime of any sort. Furthermore, it was claimed that I had deliberately blocked his way. That wasn't a crime either and again no consideration was given to the possibility that my presence in that particular place i.e. the doorway of Matthew Dodd's room, might be perfectly natural. Where was I supposed to stand when I had come up to collect the boy for his detention? They even tried to portray the fact that I had gone to collect him as some sort of crime.

With regard to the second alleged assault, Matthew Dodd was brought in as a witness. He stated that he had seen me escorting a boy from the hall. This, in fact, was the first boy, the one who had so eloquently told me to 'fuck off'. An assumption was made that this was Jim and that therefore I had made physical contact with him. The fact that this recollection didn't even fit with the boy's own description of events didn't register. He didn't claim to have been escorted out of the hall, he claimed to have been pinned against the wall and then made to wait with me until the end of break. Matthew went on to state that he had seen no form of assault take place.

He was shown a photograph of the area surrounding the hot plate and asked to state where I was in relation to this. He pointed to a place and then was asked to estimate the distance I was from the wall. He said it was three metres or so and this was immediately leapt upon by the school as evidence that I was closer to the wall than I had said. It was absolute nonsense and disregarded the fact that the photograph was taken when the hall was empty not when it was full of children who would have impeded my progress had I even tried to pin Jack against the wall.... but it didn't matter.

No one saw me assault the boy but because he said I had, despite the evidence to the contrary, then I had. He was telling the truth. I was lying. The fact that he had a motive in embellishing the truth didn't matter. To have gone to the head of year and told her that I had shouted at him would have elicited very little response – teachers shout at children all the time. Conversely, to tell her that I had grabbed him and pinned him up against a wall would give him a much stronger case.

Similarly, my assertion that discipline in the school was breaking down (and my disciplinary hearing was surely a manifestation that this was the case) fell on deaf ears and closed minds. On the subject of the school's intervention policy, Fennel admitted that there wasn't one yet... but it didn't matter. On the question of why the occupational health referral form given to Doctor Watson stated that, 'the investigation of the incidents has already been completed', Fennel replied that at the time they had been. It didn't matter that this did not correspond to subsequent events which would lead to my disciplinary hearing. They said the investigation was complete and it wasn't. It was a lie but not treated as such. Only I told lies, it seemed.

Fennel also stated that she always followed through with recommendations from Occupational Health, ignoring the fact that she had disregarded two recommendations from OH that I return to work. It didn't matter. None of it mattered. It was a sham. To even call it a kangaroo court would be to quite rightly invite condemnation from the International Kangaroo Court Council, the IKCC, an august body based in the home of the kangaroo, Sweden.

They dragged out the fact that the school had run voluntary sessions on pupil behaviour after school and that I had attended none of them. This was seen as dereliction of duty almost. Naturally, if I had attended these sessions run by some expert with extensive experience of teaching in a girl's grammar school in the sixties, then none of this would have happened. The fact that these people came in and spouted their high-sounding garbage to an audience who knew that it was nonsense but who were afraid to say so for fear of inviting the sort of unwelcome scrutiny that I was now facing, counted for nothing. These sessions were all part of the game that teachers played. The only rules were *keep your head down and agree.*

The panel had copies of 'statements' from some of my colleagues who had witnessed part of the third incident with John. On the face of it they were extremely damning, although none of them actually stated that any form of assault had occurred, simply that I had hold of the boy. In the context of this hearing, that was evidence of wrongdoing, simply because it was made to sound as if it was. Quite how a proper court would have reconciled the evidence presented to them with the charges of physical or indecent assault is a question I was never able to answer of course. Even if I had done all the things of which I was accused there would have been no need to dismiss me. The fact that I hadn't done them and that it couldn't be proved that I had, counted for nothing...

Several days later I received a letter:

'Following full and careful consideration of the facts at the panel's disposal, I must confirm that the evidence presented demonstrates that your behaviour constitutes gross misconduct. As such, the school is unable to continue with your employment and I have no alternative but to confirm your summary dismissal from your position with immediate effect.'

Chapter Seven

Life goes on

It's hard not to fall back on safe, reliable, easily understood clichés when recounting how I felt upon reading that letter. It would be altogether naff to suggest that it felt like I had been hit in the stomach with a sledgehammer, for instance, so I won't. But it did.

Those words meant that hope was gone. I was no longer able to hold out for a favourable verdict, there was no mitigation, no clemency, nothing. At once I was guilty, not merely accused. They said I was guilty, had put it in writing, therefore I was. It was no longer a case of unseen people, friends and colleagues saying, 'he must have done *something*', it was a plain old fact. Now they could say, 'I knew he did it'. Oddly, no-one was saying anything because no-one knew. To my erstwhile colleagues I hadn't been sacked, I had just disappeared. After nearly eleven years of valuable service I had simply gone and no-one noticed, such was the impact that I had made. Those teachers who think that they will be remembered after they have gone are mistaken. I had risen without trace and sunk in the same way.

The letter did not spell out any reasons for my dismissal. It might as well have said 'we sacked you because we felt like it.' If I was going to appeal I would be ignorant of the exact grounds for the decision they had taken and about which I would have to contend. As things stood I could summon only a general view that my sacking was wrong. This was just par for the course for me. I was a lay person and had been kept in the dark as much as possible right from the start. Arguably Martin should have picked up on this omission and made an approach to the school or the authority but perhaps he was too used to LEA inveigling to see any point to such action.

There were lots of things I didn't know at the time but which I later found out. One was that the witnesses against me had had no idea that they were anything of the sort. Not only did they not know that their testimony had been damning but they didn't know it had been testimony... I bore them a great deal of ill-will at the time. These people had been my friends.

'What's wrong, Daddy?', asked Grace. Evidently, I couldn't even keep my feelings private from a three-year-old. I remember looking down at her and smiling at her beautiful little face and trusting blue eyes, both of which reflected hope and confidence in the future. She epitomised all that was good in the world, with a selfless charm and a ready smile. Frankly, I didn't know whether to say anything or not – she wouldn't fully understand in either case.

'Well, I've lost my job. Some people said bad things about me and I can't be a teacher any more', I said. She smiled a little and accepted what I had said at face value. Life would go on but it would be different. The short walk to nursery from the car left me feeling winded as if a tight girdle had been pulled across my chest. The banter that we enjoyed seemed stale and pointless this morning. Grace's father wasn't a teacher any longer; he was unemployed and disgraced. I was a violent bully who picked on children. You could say anything you liked along those lines and it was true now, even though it wasn't.

Martin Fisher received the judgement at the same time as I did, and we made contact to begin the next phase of the campaign. On a number of occasions I made the trip to Bolton to talk to him, and although his pessimism remained undiminished, he agreed that we would appeal against the decision. This was done by letter and I handed it in to school, collecting a signature from the person at the reception desk, lest it be claimed that no letter had been received. I was no longer confident that my treatment would be fair or my dealings with these people, honest. Perhaps they *had* been both honest and fair throughout... but it didn't feel like it. I knew that I had been scrupulously honest – there was nothing for me to lie about, no witnesses I could bully, no statements to alter, nothing to misrepresent. Such luxuries were only afforded to the school authorities, should they choose to abuse them.

Which I am sure they didn't, by the way.

It was time for me to start again. I was confident that I could get a job. I had a lot going for me, if you overlooked the small matter of my recent sacking for gross misconduct. For starters I was still young (well, forty-three. Does that qualify?). Having shed nearly two stones I wasn't overweight. I had five 'O' levels, two GCSEs, three 'A' levels, a degree and a post-graduate certificate in education. The latter was admittedly about as much use to me now as an HND in Igloo Construction but nevertheless I had it. They couldn't take it away from me, only my need for it. In addition to my other fine qualities, such as shiny shoes and the ability to put razor sharp but ultimately rather pointless creases in shirt sleeves, I had a fine and varied work record.

For instance, I had been a soldier and thus I could kill people with both semi-automatic and automatic weapons: versatile. I could dig holes and make things look clean (which is not the same as cleaning things).

I could march, which came in handy once a year when I attended the remembrance service at the cenotaph in Preston. I could put fires out or stand in the rain for long periods of time on guard duty. I could climb over small obstacles unaided or large obstacles with the help of a few like-minded people. Even at forty-three I was sure that I could do these things, but it might take longer and be more painful. Or seem more pointless.

I had done other things. I'd been a security guard and a dishwasher but not at the same time. I had been a civil servant, giving money to people, many of whom deserved it. What else? I'd worked at Blackpool Pleasure Beach as an unsmiling drone. I had been a temporary Admin Assistant in the Employment Service both finding and losing people's claims. There was no skills shortage with me.

Even if my next position wasn't a particularly high-flying one I'd be sure to get something, but just in case and to make sure that my National Insurance Contributions were paid, I signed on with my former employers, the Employment Service. Sensibly I made my way down to the nearest office and explained my situation, but they gave me a telephone number to ring and sent me back home. I'm sure it made perfect sense to someone.

I was able to start my claim and also to make an appointment to see someone at the office I had just been turned away from. Now was not the time to rail against the idiocy of the system – I needed the system.

My interviewer at the office was very nice, neither overly solicitous nor unbearably judgemental. She listened to my brief description of events and then ran through the sponging procedure. I don't think I even bothered to explain to her that I hadn't actually done the things for which I had lost my job. What was the point? She had probably heard similar tales a thousand times and assumed that, in most cases at least, the sacking was deserved. No smoke without fire. It's hard to get away from that mentality and I am guilty of it myself. When I used to hear about miscarriages of justice or mistrials I used to think, 'well they must have done something'. As a teacher I heard children complain about their treatment at the hands of other teachers. 'Well, you must have done something to upset Mr, Mrs, Miss, Ms....' It's human nature but not very nice when you are on the receiving end of it.

We compiled a brief list of jobs that I should be searching for. Firstly, I should be looking for a teaching job. I was dubious about this but it had a certain logic - I wasn't *officially* barred from my profession, only tacitly, although the effect would be the same. I couldn't imagine even getting an interview for a job or of sitting in my prospective employer's office as he or she looked over my application and saying, 'I see you were sacked for gross misconduct. You sound like just the type of person we're looking for.'

Logically, however that really had to go on the list because I was still a teacher by profession. One never knew, my application may slip through the net somehow... Next, we put down clerical work for I had considerable experience, if not aptitude, in that department also. My career as a civil servant had not been a brilliant one; mediocre at best, punctuated with moments of dazzling adequacy. I had worked on one particular benefit managing a caseload of claims that I could only get through if I worked from the minute the office opened to the time it shut. This built up an impressive amount of 'flexi-time', which, if used, created an absence of such duration that my caseload grew back again as some sort of muffled, papery explosion. I was too plodding and methodical but still managed to make mistake after mistake. Every so often a claim would be sent off to another section whose job was basically to find fault with how it was awarded and sadly they nearly always found fault with my claims. The point of it all eluded me.

My third transferable skill was that of security guard. I had done this job in Belfast during the troubles and wore a big peaked cap with an enamel badge with the letter 'C' on it. The manager told me that the 'C' stood for c**t, because that's what you looked like when you wore the hat. In all honesty it wasn't a hard job, just as well bearing in mind what we got paid. I remember one of my colleagues bringing in a newspaper cutting with a story about delivery boys and girls going on strike because they only got £2 an hour. He showed it to the owner and we all had a laugh. Ho, ho etc. We were paid £1.65 an hour.

I had reprised this role in the flats to which my then girlfriend and I fled when we were forced out of our home. I did a fourteen-hour shift on a Sunday but actually quite enjoyed it, mainly because I was generally left alone. Who doesn't want a job like that? Sadly, things had changed since those heady days of unregulated security. The security guard of the twenty-first century has to go on a course and pay for their SIA licence before they can get a job. It has come to something when you have to be trained to drink coffee and sleep with your feet up on a desk.

All in all, my three job choices were pretty hopeless but there was some good news. Despite my wife's high wage, I was actually entitled to benefit payments due to the fact that I had contributed to the pot for many years. This slightly pleasing discovery was tempered with the possibility that my benefit might be suspended because I had been sacked – as if I had done it deliberately! For more details refer to the 'Handbook for Life', the chapter entitled, 'Kicking someone when they are down'.

As it transpired I was not considered scurrilous enough to have my payments suspended and so I joined the proud ranks of the unemployed. It wasn't my first time but nor was it my natural state. To be honest, although I wasn't proud of my new status, I wasn't ashamed of it either. Unemployment Benefit – sorry, Jobseekers Allowance (mustn't lose sight of one's ultimate aim i.e. to get a job) – was designed for people like me who had fallen on hard times. I had put in much more than I ever took out and so it was there for me just as intended. I think that the Labour Government of Clement Attlee always gets the credit for this innovation, but it was actually the Conservatives of the thirties who introduced it. It's unfashionable to credit the Tories with anything so, so... working class!

Anyway, there it was: teacher to beggar. Did I despair? Not quite. On my long runs I would have some fairly dark thoughts but I still believed that something good would come of it all... I would have to wait a long time but it did come right. I was still able to count my blessings, chief amongst them my family. I had a wife who stuck by me and two beautiful girls who just loved me for the fact that I was their dad. Life was far from perfect but other people had it worse. Of course, some people had it better as well.

So far, we'd had a pretty miserable 2009 so we decided that we would take our usual family camping holiday in France. This year we were on a budget, our joint income slashed in half, and so we stayed in the north of the country and lived as cheaply as we could. The girls and the dog enjoyed it but Diane and me? We felt the strain. It – 'that situation' – was just part of us for that whole time. It wasn't just the loss of a job; it was a loss of reputation. Who was I now? I was, officially at least, some sort of villain. I could tell people what had really happened but I didn't have a piece of paper that said 'the bearer of this letter is a good man who deserves our best wishes'.

Conversely, those who had brought this about had an actual or virtual piece of paper which said the opposite. The victors write the history books...

For now, I felt like I was deemed to be one grade above a paedophile. I was disgraced but I clung to the knowledge that I hadn't done anything wrong, although even this was scant comfort at times. We did the usual holiday things: going for walks, trips to the beach, ice creams, McDonalds. In the evening Diane and I drank wine and chatted as we always did but the whole experience felt empty, devoid of joy. The plans for the future which we usually made, some of which came to fruition and some of which faded away, didn't even feature as if there was no future for us. It was hard to see a way out. If I didn't somehow clear my name I would never teach again and frankly that was the highest paid job that I could ever hope to get. Without a job how could we finish the extension, or pay the mortgage, or go on holiday, or change the car?

We'd survive but I would always be that man who was sacked, that man 'who must have done something wrong'. You don't get the sack for no reason, do you?

When it got colder in the evenings we would sit in the porch of the tent and read but it felt as if there was someone else with us, someone who sat in judgement of me, who watched me and made notes. I couldn't really be trusted – I harmed children.

I knew that when I returned I would be hunting for a job. That was okay. I'd get something, maybe start on a second career. It would take time but I could establish myself somewhere else, begin again and rebuild my reputation. In a few years my difficulties would be forgotten about. What I really wanted was to become a writer, but I had been trying to get published for years with not even a hint of success. I hadn't even got to the point where my hopes had built up only to be dashed. Still, forget that for now, I told myself – think small but aim high. Maybe this was an opportunity in disguise – a very heavy disguise, admittedly. Maybe this situation was fate's way of pushing me off in another direction, forcing me to strike out for another career, opening the gates to a whole new world of opportunity, making me seize life by the scruff of the neck and turn things around to suit me.

Or maybe I was just unemployed.

I remembered when I had left university, armed with high hopes, enthusiasm and a 2/2 in a subject which no-one had ever heard of, I assumed that the world was my ostrich. Being shallow, materialistic and clueless, I had decided that I wanted a job where I wore a suit (not necessarily the one my mum had got from War on Want), drove a Saab and earned £30,000 a year. Quite why I had settled on this arbitrary figure of £30,000 I can't recall – it must have sounded a lot at the time. I never even gave much thought as to what the job that brought with it these bountiful gifts might be; just some sort of generic 'good job'. At the time anything seemed like a 'good job', compared to being a soldier which was the only thing I had ever done before. For instance, a job which didn't involve going to Iraq was a good job, or at least had the makings of one.

Talk about deluded. Who did I think I was? I had applied for the British Antarctic Survey (not a chance), the US Coastguard (not a chance), the Israeli Army (do me a favour, missus) and the Sea Life centre in Blackpool. I was somewhat unrealistic in my expectations. What I needed was some demoralising career advice, be that advice in demoralising careers or simply advice on careers that would leave me demoralised; there was a fine line. The question was then, as it was now: what was I suited to? I don't know how many people have the luxury of choosing a job to which they are suited but that doesn't alter the fact that the attempt should be made to match skills to needs. The problem was that some of my strengths were weaknesses. Being forthright rarely gains plaudits. Sticking to the rules has drawbacks. Being punctual is a waste of time. Being organised only puts you at a disadvantage. In a world where all too often bluffers were kings and queens, my attributes were old-fashioned and comical, laughable rather than laudable. So what else did I have to offer?

I needed something with the following 'person specification'. 'We are looking to appoint someone who is morose, disillusioned, mistrusting and curt. Ideally, we are seeking someone who is disdainful of authority and who is able to ridicule those vacuous half-wits whose wordy, worthy bombast will dictate the manner in which every small task is to be performed.' Person specifications usually contained words like 'enthusiastic' and 'motivated', thus closing the door to people like me. I was reliable, dogged even, but my enthusiasm had always been a measured thing even before the travails of life had taken their toll. I'd had cause to distrust enthusiastic people in the past; talk and no substance. I preferred to show my worth through my actions rather than my words but when applying for jobs you only have the words to rely upon, sadly.

My CV was pitifully out of date but still a collection of boastful half-truths. I hated CVs; there was no section allocated for self-deprecating honesty or the opportunity to prove that you were actually slightly better at something than you claimed. I might struggle to live up to even the most modest claims. Still my CV had plenty of variety so there would be something there that someone wanted.

At first, I applied for jobs in schools, either teaching or something similar, such as cover supervisor. The applications were lengthy, time consuming things and constantly applying was a repetitive business. It wasn't too soul-destroying to begin with because I had hope but as time went on it became an ordeal. Really, I knew that no-one was going to give me a job in a school – why would they? When I gave details of my last job the question, 'reason for leaving', was always asked and I could only reply, 'dismissed'. 'Dismissed' might have sounded slightly better than 'sacked' but it meant the same thing. I could imagine the headteacher of a school looking at my application and shaking their head shortly before dropping it in the bin.

They could have a bright-eyed young thing, dripping with enthusiasm, bursting with eagerness and (pass the sick bucket) 'wanting to make a difference' or me; early forties, world-weary and something of a hand-me-down relic. For £20,000 they could have a youngster oozing buzz words and educational jargon or for £35,000 someone who knew how to teach but who had been sacked for doing so. These were easy choices. Rarely did an applicant give them the opportunity to shorten their short-list with such ease. I applied for a job as registrar at the college in which I had trained to be a teacher but received no sort of acknowledgement.

I applied for other types of jobs too. 'Night extruder operator' in a pet food factory was one. I had never extruded at night, or during the day come to that and, truth be told, had no idea what this job might entail. I imagined that it would involve tipping huge buckets of partly-butchered animal carcasses into a hot, bubbling vat of something indescribable and then stirring it with a mechanical device called a spondulator that resembled a giant whisk. Most likely I would have to wear green overalls, white wellies and a mask to make me look like some cut-price surgeon. My clothes and hair would stink of hot offal, a condition which would gradually become permanent as the constant slippy-slop of mortal remains soaked through my skin and into my very soul. I was looking forward to this new career but never even got an interview.

What was missing from my CV? What made them think I wasn't up to the job? Was it the case that they were simply inundated with applications from existing extruder operators or did they meet their extrusion needs in some other way? Perhaps I would have been a rotten extruder operator but we will never know. Presumably I was setting my sights too high; maybe I should have been looking for trainee extruder operator positions first and then getting experience...

This sort of disappointment became the norm. I had fallen a long way. Another job for which I applied was taking orders for a fresh fruit and veg company at night. With my experience of using a phone (we even have our own phone in the house) I thought that I was ideally qualified, even before you took into account my knowledge of fruit. I could name six or seven different types of fruit and identify many of these by sight. Admittedly I wasn't so hot on vegetables; I can't tell an anchovy from an iguana. I didn't get an interview but I did get an acknowledgement of my application which I took as some sort of encouragement – at least I still existed. I could really see myself doing that job: sleeves rolled up, hot cup of coffee steaming gently as I flipped through fruit recognition charts with one hand, scribbling out the order form with the other and the phone clamped between cheek and shoulder. High pressure... I would be a fruit executive. Maybe not.

I applied to be a meter reader, a career that promised much for the right kind of person. Was I prepared to go out in all weathers? Yes, I was. Did I like meeting people? Not really but I could do it if I had to. In return for this you got a salary and a little car to go about in. Sadly, I must not have been the 'right kind of person'.

Was I dismayed? Frankly, yes, but I had no option but to go on. Every two weeks I would make my way down to the unemployment office with my pathetic list of job applications. I kept a record of dates applied and dates responded to, the latter being largely blank. I met a different person each week and explained to them what efforts I had made and then they looked for some suitable jobs for me on their computer. I would then go home, apply for these jobs and some others, and then return to the office still unemployed. On the bright side, I still had my health.

Security jobs were a dead end, but I did write to my old employers in the flats to see if they would contact me if any positions came up. I never heard back. I registered with various employer's websites. Particularly impressive was the local council one which enabled me to put in my details and then use these repeatedly for different jobs. Each time I applied I just had to write a new covering letter. I applied for library jobs, van drivers, road repair, quite a few really, some of which I quite fancied. From this I heard not one word.

I applied to jobs in the NHS and heard not one word. I applied to become an ironing person. Nothing. I applied for several cleaning jobs. Nothing. I asked the man who had built our extension if he needed a labourer but he was resolutely a one-man band.

I applied to be an NVQ assessor. For this I had a bit of inside help, knowing someone who knew someone who already worked there... It seemed like a good job; decent wage, company car. I allowed my hopes to be built up.

Nothing.

I applied for a job with the Royal British Legion, of which I had been a member for quite a few years. I knew I was in with a real chance here with a good understanding of the Legion's aims and experience in administration. In some ways I was ideal.

Nothing.

I applied for a job as a cleaner in an office building. A few days later I drove past it to discover that it had been shut down and needless to say the job never materialised.

I applied for a job working in the Spar warehouse where, apparently, they were 'always taking people on'.

Nothing.

I applied for a job as a temporary librarian at the University; well, you know I didn't get it. I found a scheme for tutoring schoolchildren and joined that, seeming to be accepted... if *not* being overtly turned down can be taken as 'acceptance'. To this day I have not tutored anyone.

A teaching supply agency seemed to offer me some hope. I attended an interview and was completely open about my past experiences. In return my interviewer was completely open about my chances of getting work, which is not to say he was entirely pessimistic. The fact was that he would have to make a case for me, just to get started but once I had done some work, if I built a good reputation then more work would follow. Schools would often ask if a particular teacher was available when the need arose because they knew that he or she could come in and do the job well within the strictures of supply teaching at least. Once I had got going then my past was history and largely irrelevant. The rate of pay was good and it seemed as if I once again had hope, although I had previously stated that I would never under any circumstances become a supply teacher.

Supply teachers at Collegiate always had a tough time, many of them refusing ever to come back. Frequently their lessons would be absolute chaos, the room in which they had been 'teaching' devastated at the end. Supply teachers were easy meat, lacking the standing of the permanent teachers in the school – that's just how it was. Now I was set to join their ranks and I was not confident at all. I imagined myself standing impotently as a tornado of mischief tore up the room around me. The years I had spent building up my reputation would count for nothing, my tricks of the trade rendered obsolete, and I would be a mere accessory to ruin... but that is what I had become already. Whoever I had been as a teacher had departed long before I physically left the building for the last time. I thought about the confrontations I would have as a supply teacher: telling children to get on with their work, asking them why they were late, why they were messing about, telling them not to throw their books out of the window, not to run around, not to run out of the room, not to set fire to the person next to them. There was an endless list of petty misdemeanours I would have to contend with and it could only end with humiliation.

Within a short time, the agency had rung me to ask if I would be interested in teaching in Cumbria. I said that I would although this would involve me staying in a hotel or B and B, eating into my wage. They'd ring me back to let me know... I'm still waiting. Should I assume that I have been unsuccessful? I paid for my own CRB and it came back stating that I had no criminal convictions but that I had been dismissed, although I was appealing the decision. It was hardly a glowing endorsement.

Chapter Eight

Appeal

My appeal was scheduled for early October 2009. Martin Fisher and I had already discussed the probable need for a tribunal as my next recourse, although he was very pessimistic both about my chances of success and the chances of the NUT supporting me. The news was generally grim. I was fighting for my reputation but without much hope that it could be restored. However, there was nothing else I could do. I had to keep going. I am sure the school was dismayed that I hadn't simply given up but there was no chance of that and never would be.

I had already begun the next stage of my defence by contacting the Employment Tribunals Service, something which had to be done within three months of the decision to sack me. Martin and I had both realised that my appeal date fell three days beyond this limit, and I suspected that this was a deliberate subterfuge. 'Have they done this on purpose?' I asked. He gave me a knowing look. 'They won't even know that you have applied for a tribunal yet. It'll be a nasty surprise for them.' Had the approaching time limit not become apparent to one or other of us, I would naturally have waited for the outcome of the appeal before applying to the Tribunals Service. It was illogical not to do so but I explained to them why such a move was necessary.

It was a depressing time and a considerable strain both for me and for Diane, who had also begun a new job in September. This new job proved to be the beginning of the end for the case against me. As head of year seven she happened to meet one of the witnesses whose statement had apparently suggested that I had assaulted John outside Matthew Dodd's classroom. Sara was there with her partner John, neither of whom worked at Collegiate any longer. She was attending an open evening to see if Diane's new school was suitable for one of her children and John recognised my wife. Sara approached to ask how I was but got a rather frosty reception, Diane holding her, in part, responsible for my undoing. This was a pivotal moment. From here on in things slowly began to turn in my favour, although I had a great many more setbacks to endure.

As they chatted, Sara concerned, Diane angry, a number of things became clear. The first of these was that Sara had no idea that I had been sacked. No-one did. Secondly, she had no idea that she was a witness against me. She never knew about the case that had been constructed to bring about my dismissal or about her part in it. Gradually she became aware of the reasons for Diane's less than warm treatment and they talked for some time when Diane should really have been meeting the parents of prospective pupils.

The news was the first indication that someone actually believed or knew that I had been telling the truth, and as the encounter was replayed upon Diane's return home that evening I have to admit that I cried. Not only did Sara know the truth of what had happened but she was willing to testify on my behalf. It seemed as if the tide might have begun to turn. Sara now, with some reluctance, for by her own admission she was afraid of her former headteacher, agreed to attend the appeal and to prepare a statement which she could read out. This would have to be done quickly, as anything of this nature would have to be formally submitted as evidence but I am sure that it came as something of a shock to Fennel to find that one of her witnesses was now turning on her.

As Diane further recalled the incident I was touched when she mentioned something that Sara's partner, John had said along the lines of 'Dave was one of the few that did what he was told and tried to maintain discipline. It was everyone else that let him down'. That may have been overstating the case but

I did feel that there was more than a grain of truth in what he said; that is certainly how I had viewed my conduct in the school – conduct which had cost me my job.

If Diane's news offered me a distinct glimmer of hope, the next news delivered what I thought might be the knockout blow to my opponents. A text from Matthew Dodd told me that Fennel had been removed from her post as headteacher. No-one quite knew why but she would be leaving within a few days to take up an advisory post with the education authority – a sideways move to keep her out of trouble. Naturally, I assumed that the governors or someone was dissatisfied with her handling of my case and that this was an indication that I would get my job back. Excitedly, I told Martin Fisher but he was dubious. He doubted that that was the case and as it turned out he was right.

I can't say that I didn't derive some sort of base pleasure from hearing about her downfall. The only thing she had in her life was that school and now it had been taken from her in a rather ignominious fashion. I heard later that she had bumped into one of my old colleagues, now retired, and had enthused about her new advisory job, claiming that it was so good she 'had to take it'. She was partly right; she did have to take it! When we met again I'm sure that the irony of the situation was not lost on her.

Naturally, the appeal took place in the memorial room and this time a different set of governors were assembled. This alone, I thought, gave me some hope, never mind my new witness and Fennel's downfall. Bundles of documents exchanged hands and everything was done without my opponents having any knowledge of the fact my application for a tribunal was submitted and being processed. They must surely have thought that this was my final attempt at securing justice and that I would desist when my appeal was unsuccessful; that was what the script dictated at least. Most people in my situation, I think, rolled over and gave in to the inevitable.

There were a number of odd aspects to the appeal. For instance, the school was now calling a number of witnesses, something which they had not done previously and in truth should not have done now. The purpose of the appeal was to examine if the correct decision had been made by the disciplinary panel, not to re-examine the case itself. New witnesses suggested that the latter rather than the former was happening.

One of these witnesses was Matthew Dodd, who had previously been one of my witnesses! Clearly, they thought that his previous testimony, in which he had placed me closer to the canteen wall than was the case, was so damaging that his inclusion would drive the panel to the required decision. In addition, they called upon Allyson England, who, along with

Sara was one of the witnesses to the incident with John. She would be there to support her original statement. Polly Summerlee was called to verify that her version of events with Jim was correct because of her thorough re-visiting of the facts.

Another witness, Wendy Casson, was also called. Unlike your average witness at a court case or similar, she had not actually witnessed anything but was there at Gill Fennel's behest to explain that I was a thoroughly bad egg with a history of violent conduct towards children. She had no evidence of this, no written record, no hearsay evidence, no complaints from children, no disciplinary action taken by her or anyone else with regard to this bad conduct but her say-so was enough. She was a sort of reverse character witness.

In a proper court I am quite sure that the judge would be questioning what her attendance was actually designed to do, but this wasn't a proper court. Like the disciplinary hearing that had gone before it didn't even adhere to basic principles of justice.

The panel comprised the chair of governors, Steve Wenman, who was also acting as chair of the appeal panel, and two other governors. To say that Wenman was impartial was stretching the definition of that word to its very limits. For instance, he had sent a letter to staff and parents on the Christmas preceding my suspension, in which he had obsequiously praised the Head, comparing her to Captain Janeway, the fictional commander of the equally fictional Star Trek Voyager. He even suggested that the school could perhaps be re-named Starship Collegiate. He continued in this vein of fawning prose for an entire sick-making page of A4 before signing off, 'Regards Steve'. There was even a little cartoon of himself at the top of the page. The whole thrust of the letter was how well Fennel had done in leading the school. Even those who were rarely to be drawn on the subject of the school's obvious decline scoffed at this ridiculous missive.

His view about how well things were going proved to be at odds with a report produced by an organisation called 'Pygmalion' which gave the staff an opportunity to voice their opinion about the state of the school anonymously. I, as an ex-employee, wasn't privy to any of its findings and it proved remarkably hard to track down a copy but the staff interviewed indicated that poor behaviour was a significant problem in the school and that the senior management were held in low esteem. This was precisely what I had told the Head in my March interview. Fennel called a staff meeting to give feedback on the findings of the Pygmalion report but was apparently very curt with the teachers and dismissive of the report's contents. It was ever thus when it came to bad news...

Martin tried to draw the other side out about the report, which neither of us had seen, but there was a great deal of reticence in this regard. The information contained therein would have been mitigating of my conduct but whilst they stopped short of denying its existence they certainly played down its importance.

My witnesses consisted of a very nervous Sara Maddox and my old friend Anne, the former school governor who had worked for years in the science department of which I too had been a member. She acted as a character witness.

Another interesting little cameo was played out as I waited in reception for Martin Fisher's arrival. It was odd to be a guest (a not especially welcome one) in what had been my place of work for over ten years. I didn't know the lady on the reception desk – she was new – and she didn't know me. Just a year earlier I had been part of the furniture almost and now I was a stranger. Even now as I describe the following event I do so with some trepidation – not worried for myself but for the other party involved; vestigial paranoia, I would call it. As I waited pensively, one of my erstwhile colleagues came from the office. He smiled and said hello. I stood as we shook hands and we chatted briefly. He was shocked to learn that I had been sacked and then did something which turned matters on their head.

Furtively he retrieved a piece of paper from the front desk and scribbled a name and number on it.

'This is someone who can help you but don't say that you got it from me', he said. I could see genuine concern on his face. He knew that helping me would be very bad for his career. I took the paper and slipped it away for future use. We parted and then Martin arrived. My second date with destiny was about to commence. My confidence was higher than it had been. The presence of a witness who would state that I had not assaulted anyone would surely save me.

I recapped, as I often did; one allegation from which I had been exonerated, one which had no witnesses and one with a witness who would state that no assault had occurred; what could go wrong? Throw in Fennel's recent removal from post and two doctor's reports which stated that I was medically fit for a return to work and I was obviously home and dry. Martin Fisher didn't think so. I couldn't understand why. We walked along the corridor to the memorial room like the condemned man and his priest, an analogy which I hoped developed no further.

Formal introductions were made but the names were lost to me as soon as they had been delivered. On the right side of Wenman sat a female governor and on his left a male governor, both relatively young, as was Wenman himself. I hoped that these two would offer me some hope, would listen to the evidence and make the correct decision. They might be genuinely impartial but I feared that Wenman's word would carry the day... and I already knew what outcome he had decided upon. Quite apart from his unquestioning and misplaced adoration of the Headteacher, he had a peculiar reputation, with a great many strange habits and interests being attributed to him. One of these was that he had spent his entire adult life in further education of one sort or another, gaining qualification after qualification without ever repaying the state's beneficence by getting a job afterwards.

Recently however, he had qualified as a nurse and he never missed an opportunity to tell people that this was so. Not only had he qualified but, in a break with tradition, he had actually got a job as a nurse. To hear him talk one might think that he had spent his life working, like the rest of us, although to be fair the sheer novelty of labour and of earning money, paying taxes et cetera must have made it hard for him to resist discussing his new career. He was enthusiastic about work in a way which few people of his age could ever hope to match.

In addition to studying he had purportedly fathered a great many children, at least three of whom came to the school of which he was chair of governors. On occasion, I am told, he strayed and was once banished to a caravan on the driveway of his rather capacious council house. Legend had it that he was a white witch. I don't know what white witches do and I am not even slightly tempted to find out, not even for the purposes of this book. What I do know and what is an indisputable fact is that a female colleague of mine once caught him coming out of the ladies' toilets next to the staff room. Now that isn't normal. As for the rest of it, I don't know if it's all true or not. Was Mr Wenman very weird? I couldn't say.

The room was packed with the usual HR people, governors and so on. It felt very much like Martin Fisher and I versus the world, although I am forgetting that many of these people were impartial and only interested in justice being done. How silly of me. Again, my mind was a sort of emotional blank. There was nothing for me to do but listen as my reputation was viciously torn asunder like a Christian thrown to the lions. Even then the Christian had more of a fighting chance than I had; the lions might be having an off day or simply not be hungry, whereas I was there so that my guilt could be established for a second time. Had it not been for the fact that it was my conduct under scrutiny and my future in the balance, the whole process might have been very interesting. The questions asked and the looks and the note taking seemed to give an indication as to my jury's feelings.

Wenman was combative, dismissive and eager to get things over with. It was clear that for him, this was a formality and a rather inconvenient one at that. This sort of thing was obviously not what he had signed up for when he had decided to become chair of governors. I was simply being awkward. The truth of this became even more apparent in the months ahead.

He pointedly looked at his watch on a number of occasions and even mentioned that he had another appointment to go to when this was finished. I even heard him ask how long these things normally took. None of these acts inspired confidence in the process which would decide my fate. I hadn't expected him to take my side or even be ambivalent, but I truly did not expect him to make his disdain for me and my life quite so obvious. By contrast the other two governors seemed fairer, asking questions that seemed to be aimed at establishing the truth. At one point the female governor even shot a faint smile my way as if to say, 'don't worry'. Would these people prove to be my salvation? No, in a word.

The witnesses trailed in one after the other, sheepishly, ebulliently, nervously. It was their job to praise me or to damn me. I was entirely passive, a victim. It was a little drama acted out about me and for me. In its previous showing I clearly hadn't understood the essential message – you're sacked – and so it had been refined and re-modelled so that I would be fully aware of all the pertinent facts that had led to the original denouement.

Martin was 'up' first, because it was for us to prove that the original decision had been wrong. This put us at a disadvantage since we could only make our case once and then wait until our opponents tried to destroy it. Again, Martin began with the point that the first incident should never have been taken into consideration and again the school fell back on the word 'safeguarding' and all its implications. He talked about the fact that the investigation was flawed and had taken too long. He mentioned that witness statements were not taken or taken incorrectly and that with regard to the second incident in the dinner hall Fennel relied completely on Mrs Summerlee's second hand accounts of what had occurred.

He argued that there were instances where teachers were allowed to restrain children and that my use of restraint had not been examined with the appropriate guidelines in mind. He highlighted yet more inconsistencies in Jim's testimony: in one version of events he is thrown against a wall and in another he is pushed against the wall; in one he is grabbed by the neck and in another held by the front of his blazer. Of course, in regard to this my version of events was never even asked for, let alone considered.

Martin again mentioned my mental health as being a mitigating circumstance. Again, I disagreed strongly on this point. If we were claiming that I was innocent (which I was) then what did my health have to do with it? It was illogical to me. 'He didn't do it, but he wasn't thinking clearly at the time', or 'he didn't do it but if he had then it would have been because he had mental health issues'. It's like a crime of passion without the crime. Much later he would explain why he took this approach. He knew that the odds were so stacked against me that only by pulling out every possible factor, every fragment of mitigation could he hope to salvage something. Martin didn't think I was guilty, just that I was doomed.

Martin referred to testimonials from the local police constable in my village and from Anne Roberts both of which stated that I was a reliable and honest person. A photocopied extract from my army service book was examined and it too seemed to suggest that I was a decent man.

Next came Anne's personal testimony about my good character. She was not cowed or intimidated by the assembled group and knew me better than anyone else in the room. I was very touched by what she said. She related the time I had conducted an experiment into water divining and the fact that I had established a model making club for waifs at lunchtime. She said that I was one of the few teachers who consistently applied the rules and supported the school's aims despite the difficulties that I would encounter as a result of doing so. Nor did I suffer fools gladly, according to Anne and, although I shouted at pupils, she had never seen me do anything which could result in physical harm. Despite my dismal circumstances I smiled at the recollection of the water divining experiment...

My wife's Mum's husband (whom she had never thought of as a step-father, hence my awkward description of him) had worked on a farm in his youth and he told me how they would find underground springs by divining with a wire coat hanger shaped like a wishbone. I decided to use one of my classes to see if this method of finding water had any merit; as a scientist I was sceptical but open-minded – if that makes sense. My room at the time had old fashioned wooden benches with square sinks loaded with broken stationery, chewing gum and sundry unspeakable items, all deposited there through a tiny hole in the removable wooden, sink covers. Periodically, the technicians would don their rubber gloves and remove the accumulated detritus, a glamorous job and no mistake.

For my great experiment these sinks would serve as my hidden springs and so I blocked half the plug holes, filled them with water and sealed the covers down with tape to deter prying eyes. The remainder of the sinks I left empty but sealed down their lids also.

I discovered that wire coat hangers are fairly difficult to get these days but managed to find enough to produce a class set of diviners. After the briefest possible explanation of the task my pupils set about conducting the experiment. In a sense this was proper science because they were testing something about which no definitive answer (to my knowledge) had ever been found; if it did work, no-one knew why. Children generally enjoyed practical work, although sometimes for the wrong reasons, and this task was no different. I had chosen – euphemism alert – a 'well-motivated' group to avoid the sort of debacle I might otherwise expect, involving sword fights and discreet but malicious torture.

Children could generally find uses for pieces of equipment other than those intended by the manufacturer and these tended to have some destructive or dangerous subtext, hence my doubts about people when they say they 'loved science at school'. Real science is often difficult and painstaking, the excitement coming from the results rather than the means by which they were achieved. Those who 'loved science at school' may simply be recalling the joy of misusing a Bunsen burner or of mixing chemicals together in some illicit way. Even I hadn't loved science at school and I had by a rather circuitous route finished up being a science teacher. There is an expectation that goes from generation to generation that science lessons will inevitably involve explosions of various types.

Admittedly for me and my cohort we didn't actually hanker after this at all, a fact which I can only explain as being a by-product of living in Northern Ireland, home of the explosion. We still did the other ridiculous things like sticking our pens down the barrel of the Bunsen or melting our rulers. In those days too, we had sharpeners made from magnesium, which burnt vigorously when heated in a Bunsen flame. None of this was sufficient to engender a love of science in me.

The children conducted the experiment in an orderly way and made a record of each time their divining equipment dipped down in the requisite manner to indicate the presence of water in an 'underground spring'. Their results were then collated in one huge table on the board and conclusions drawn.

Astonishingly, our findings seemed to indicate that water divining was no old wives' tale. Whilst we couldn't offer definitive proof of anything from our study, the diviners did seem to dip down in the presence of water more often than not. It was rare that the chance to do any original science ever presented itself but the children enjoyed it and learnt about analysing data.

The origins of my old model making club also sprang to mind upon Anne's mention of it. From my desk I could see out onto the playground and remember one little year seven boy who paced its circumference every lunchtime, seemingly friendless and perhaps lost in a little world that existed only in his head where he found refuge from the sometimes intimidating rough and tumble of 1500 pupils, high on 'E' numbers. I wondered what could be done for gentle souls such as him and hit upon the idea for the model making club, a gentle pursuit and more importantly, somewhere to go or a place to belong.

He was my first member although he was joined by a few other boys later. The numbers never rose above five or six and this was about right I thought. One year a gaggle of girls turned up at my door asking about joining. I was a bit confused but after a brief discussion I realised that they were thinking of the other type of modelling. Suffice to say that I had to stifle their catwalk dreams.

Would Anne's comments make any difference? Wenman asked when she had left the school and she replied four and half years ago, the implication being that I could have become a violent monster in the interim. Carol Gee, from HR asked her if she thought I was conversant with the school's policies and procedures. Anne said that she thought I was. Gee then asked her if she herself had been conversant with them to which Anne with all the hauteur she could summon replied that having been a school governor for thirty-two years had helped to formulate those policies and procedures. Gee backed down.

In the short-term Anne may not have saved me from my fate but it was lovely to have someone so self-assured and so obviously decent in my corner. To condemn me was to condemn her in a sense.

Next up was Sara Maddox and she was summoned to the room, where she was greeted before she took her seat. Sara read her statement which is copied below with names left out.

My name is Sara Maddox. I was a teacher in the English department at Collegiate High school from September 2000 until July 2009. I am now head of English at ???????Special School in Preston.

On the 16th of December 2008, at the end of the school day, I witnessed an incident involving Mr Roy and a pupil called John *******. I will return to this later.

The following morning, as I was halfway through teaching a lesson, Mr Pomeroy came in. He said that I had to go straight away to Miss Fennel's office and that he was to cover my lesson. I asked him if he knew why and he said he didn't. I hurriedly made sure that the pupils had adequate work and went to the office. I was very nervous as nothing like this had happened before.

On entering the office Miss Fennel invited me to sit down. She asked me if I had seen an incident with Mr Roy the previous day. I said I had and we proceeded to chat about it for a minute or two. I say chat because it seemed to me a very informal discussion just to see what had happened. Not long into the conversation I became aware that Diane Martin was also in the room and that she was taking notes of what was being said. The conversation lasted no more than a couple of minutes and it was only as I was leaving that Miss Fennel told me that Ms Martin would be typing up my statement and asking me to sign it. Feeling slightly confused I went back to my lesson.

I cannot remember the exact timing of the next event but whilst teaching another lesson Ms Martin came to me with a typed-up statement and asked me to sign it. As I was very busy teaching I only cast an eye over it and signed it.

I would therefore like to make the following points about my statement:

1. Due to the fact that I was teaching I do not feel that I had adequate time to gather my thoughts about the previous day's incident.

2. I was not aware that I was giving a formal statement or that it would be used in disciplinary proceedings against Mr Roy, as at no time was this mentioned.

3. As it was a formal statement I should have been given the opportunity to write down the events that I witnessed, again to give me time to gather my thoughts and also to ensure that my statement was clear and could not be misunderstood in any way.

4. I think it was very unprofessional to be asked to sign a statement of such seriousness in a classroom full of pupils during a lesson. This also did not really give me any opportunity to read it through and make any adjustments that may have been needed.

If you take all the above points into consideration I would like to state quite firmly that I do not believe my statement to have been taken in a fair and honest way.

I believe therefore that certain points need clarifying:

1. The opening line of my statement says that 'Mr Roy had John up against the wall holding his coat'. This sounds as if Mr Roy was being aggressive when in fact John was actually using the wall to slide along whilst trying to get away, and Mr Roy was just holding onto his coat with one hand to prevent him leaving. Mr Roy was quite calm and just kept reiterating that Jack had a DT and would be staying to do it.

2. The next point that I would like to clarify is the part when John was saying 'Get off, get off.' As I said in an earlier part of the statement John was swearing a lot at Mr Roy. When he was saying 'get off' this was in a very aggressive and threatening way. As had all the swearing been. In short John was completely verbally aggressive the whole time. This leads on to the next point.

3. Due to the fact that John was being verbally aggressive and was really beginning to lose his temper I decided that it might be better to take him away and calm him down before he lashed out at Mr Roy. John is capable of that type of behaviour. In my statement I said that I 'asked Mr Roy to get off him, as did another member of staff'. At this point Mr Roy had John screaming at him as well as a number of other pupils who were shouting and jeering. I cannot be certain that Mr Roy actually heard us.

I did not shout it out but just suggested it in a normal voice so that we could try and resolve the situation in a different manner.

4. John came with me to a nearby classroom where he did calm down but kept reiterating that he was not doing the DT. I got the impression that John had never intended doing the detention and was absolutely furious that his plan not to go had been thwarted by Mr Roy coming personally to collect him before the end of the last lesson.

At no time during this incident did I feel that Mr Roy was acting unprofessionally or aggressively. If I had felt that Mr Roy was anyway wrong in the actions that he had taken I would have immediately reported the incident to the head teacher or a member of the leadership team. I did not feel then, nor have I since felt, that it was necessary to do so.

I believe Mr Roy to be an excellent teacher who is highly regarded by both the staff and pupils at Collegiate High School

Sara Maddox

It was extremely damning of course and I felt that her testimony would have unravelled the remaining scrap of dubious evidence that might just about have incriminated me. She not only stated that no assault had taken place but that her evidence had been taken in an inappropriate manner and then misused. This was the first indication by a third party that something rather sinister had taken place when it came to the case against me. Fennel had been deceitful and manipulative and in time many more examples of her less than honest approach would be uncovered.

Had these revelations occurred in court, the judge might well have smelt a rat at this point. Here was a witness for the prosecution jumping ship and casting doubt on the manner in which the investigation had been conducted. Not for the first time I was to rue the fact that my case was not being heard in court. Instead of an experienced judge with years of legal training behind him or her, I had Wenman, a trained nurse, with a penchant for science fiction and witchcraft. I suppose I should have been grateful that he didn't want to test my innocence or otherwise with a trial which ended in my death by burning or drowning. He was going to find me guilty anyway so he didn't have to bother with such refinements.

Naturally, Fennel and friends tried to undermine Sara and make her evidence seem unreliable, and in that they failed for Sara was not cowed in any way. She stuck to her story and was not swayed. At one-point Fennel complained piteously that since she operated an 'open door policy', Sara could have come to see her if she harboured any doubts. This missed the obvious point that Sara would never do this simply because she didn't know that her statement was being used as part of an investigation into my conduct. She had no reason to have doubts. In response to Fennel's assertion about her approachability, Sara said, 'I don't find you very easy to talk to'.

Fennel had acted out the role of 'people person' for so long that she was clearly discomfited by the harsh truth, something which she had been protected from by her inherited circle of sycophants. This group had no loyalty to anyone but the most recent postholder and would have deserted her already. Her world was falling apart – it was the only thing we had in common.

Again, I was touched by Sara's defence of my character. I hadn't really had anything nice said about me for some time but it would all be swept away in the deluge of thinly disguised vitriol that comprised the second part of my trial. For Fennel, Sara's words were a betrayal but the latter was no longer at the school and therefore free to tell the truth, a luxury that was not awarded to all the witnesses.

My witnesses dispensed with, it was now time for the main act. Allyson England was one of the witnesses to the incident outside Matt's classroom, the other being Sara who had already swapped sides. Now it was her turn to give evidence and she responded to a series of carefully contrived questions with a series of carefully contrived

160

answers. Her speech was stilted, unnatural and she spoke entirely without conviction. She too looked close to tears and deeply unhappy. I thought that it was clear that she was acting under duress.

I was reminded of the British aircrew shot down over Iraq in 1991, both of whom were paraded in front of the local TV cameras to read out prepared statements about the iniquity of the regime that they represented. They couldn't have been less convincing if they had tried. It was a masterpiece of tactical insincerity. Allyson was ashen-faced and obviously very unhappy. Anyone watching her performance would have realised that she simply did not believe in what she was saying. At no time did she look in my direction. A paper record of her words was more harmful to my case than her actual verbal evidence, but such a disparity was academic when minds were already made up.

Asked if she was happy with the way in which her statement had been taken, a question prompted by Sara's assertion that she personally wasn't, she replied that she was. The conflict between her words and her body language was never clearer than at that moment. I knew that she had been spoken to about where her loyalties lay and her recent promotion within the school. It would be easy to make this sound like a form of intimidation, would it not?

Matt Dodd was brought in to testify that I had been in a position to pin the boy against the wall and that I had removed him forcibly from the hall. It made no sense and his cross-examination was cut short because it began to damage their case. Matt's version of events didn't pan out or suit their objectives; they had no interest in hearing the truth from the only witness they had ever found to the second incident.

Polly Summerlee's testimony followed the well-worn path that I had admitted to my alleged assault upon Jim in the dinner hall. She said it was so and I said it was not so. They believed her. The boy in question had not changed his story, therefore it was true. I, on the other hand, had changed my story and was lying. This part of their story left me seething. I hadn't changed my story simply because I had no story to change. I had never assaulted the boy and never admitted to it and yet they blithely claimed that I had, despite not having any evidence at all. There was nothing I could do or say to counter this argument.

Under cross-examination from Martin her composure crumbled and it was clear that she lacked any clear understanding of the incident or any real belief in the version of events she was there to support. I scribbled down on a piece of paper, 'she used to think very highly of me' and shoved it discreetly Martin's way. He questioned her about her opinion of me as a teacher and a form tutor and she admitted that she thought I was a great example of each. Naturally this conflict in her testimony made no difference. Towards the end she began to cry and her involvement ended soon after.

Mrs Casson talked at length about the measures taken by the school to improve the lot of its teachers. She herself had left the previous year, perhaps not quite as enamoured with the situation at the school as she suggested. The main thrust of her argument was that I had wilfully not accepted the help that was available and also that I was a rather bad person whose conduct had warranted her intervention. The irony was that she was a rather 'hands on' type of teacher with an intimidating presence.

She had been one of the untouchables in school, her conduct not subject to the same scrutiny as other teachers, the same standards not applied. I had my own theories about why this was the case but they remained only theories.

Neath, taking responsibility for the decision made by the disciplinary panel, was required to give evidence. The decision was based on the evidence supplied, he ventured vaguely. When it became clear that he couldn't really explain why I had been dismissed, his HR advisor took over and explained it on his behalf. This was well beyond the remit of said HR adviser.

The justification for putting no weight on Sara's change of allegiance was that there were three incidents being considered, all of which formed a pattern of behaviour which made me likely to be a danger to children. I had to listen to this trite nonsense in silence, although I was screaming inside. Where was the pattern; exonerated from one incident, no witnesses to the second 'incident' and a witness stating that the third incident was not an assault? Even had I been given the opportunity to interject at this point it would have made no difference but I think I still vacillated between hope and despair; hope that justice would prevail like the melodramatic end to a courtroom drama of one man versus the system, and despair at the reality of my situation. For every argument there was, quite naturally, a counterargument. I would not have expected anything else. What was unreasonable was that these counter arguments were illogical, poorly thought out and irrelevant.

Things moved on inexorably. I was unable to gauge how we were doing beyond my suspicion that we were basically doomed. Martin forged ahead with another argument which I thought was inconsistent with the basic idea that I had done nothing wrong. He asked why it had been necessary to dismiss me when there were mitigating factors (mental health) and when I had made assurances about my future conduct. The former I have dealt with, but the latter… if I hadn't done anything wrong what guarantees could I make about future conduct? It didn't make sense. 'I am not guilty but I can guarantee that it won't happen again'. The implication is, if anything, that in future I cannot guarantee to behave in a way which will cause no harm to children... or am I being pedantic?

As each point was discussed, clarified and glossed over, there was a great deal of shuffling of paper, pointing of fingers and, for some, the silent movement of lips as they read passages from the collected evidence assembled for the hearing. Each person in the room had a small mountain, perhaps a hillock, of notes relating to witness statements, investigation notes, policies, procedures... These were referred to at the appropriate moments but it became clear that the panel, the HR bods, and Fennel (who wasn't even required to be there) were continually referring to a particular document which neither Martin nor I could locate.

It transpired that, entirely by coincidence, everyone bar Martin and I had been given a copy of the minutes of the disciplinary hearing which included, amongst other things, the reasons for the decision they had reached. It was this decision that we were contesting, but we'd had to construct our case without any knowledge of the precise reasons for their decision to dismiss. Arguably, Martin should have noticed that these were missing before. It was hard to argue in detail that the decision was wrong without knowing how it had been reached. Perhaps there was some perfectly logical reasoning involved in the decision but we simply had no idea if this was so.

Once the point had been raised, there was a break in proceedings while the panel decided if an adjournment was justified. Martin and I retired to another room. For once I detected a note of optimism in his demeanour.

'If they don't agree to an adjournment, to give us a chance to read the findings of the original panel, then we've got them', he said. I didn't quite understand. The point he was making was that that they had to give us a reasonable amount of time to consider this evidence or their case would not stick. It seemed as if I would win if that happened but only on a technicality. To win in that manner would be rather unsatisfying and would also only postpone the day when another case was fabricated against me as is surely would be... but at the time I would have settled for that.

Had everything else seemed above board and transparently honest I would have assumed that the omission of this evidence from our bundles was merely an oversight. However, the sheer volume of apparent subterfuge made me think otherwise. At all costs I was to be found guilty of, and remain guilty of, *something*.

We were granted our adjournment, something that Wenman thought we ought to be supremely grateful for – it was just another example of the school's fair-mindedness in his view. We would all meet again in a week once Martin and I had a chance to consider the information contained in the missing minutes. As we made our way across the school car park that night, each heading for his respective car, Martin remarked happily, 'we live to fight another day'. This didn't fill me with confidence. It sounded like a postponement of defeat, rather than fresh chance of victory.

In the following week I thought about my circumstances as I pounded the country roads on my run, as I cooked tea, ironed or as I was getting off to sleep. There was no avoiding such introspection, a re-examination of facts, a wilful clutching at straws. 'Living to fight another day', was not any sort of release. What had really changed? Only a change of jury could really help me now. Wenman was going to ensure that Fennel prevailed. Martin understood this well.

When we reconvened, there was a brief discussion of the minutes, but nothing had really changed. The ex-Headteacher, Fennel, was in attendance once more, although why she bothered was beyond me. Both sides summed up and we went our separate ways. Martin's demeanour as we parted told me everything I needed to know and a few days later a letter arrived to confirm that I remained sacked.

PART TWO

Chapter One

This is the End...

I suppose my life entered a new phase at that point. My association with the school was severed. I would never return. For me there would be no leaving speech, no collection and no miserable little meal out with my former colleagues. There would be no good reference either – they were rid of me and I could be thrown to the wolves with impunity. My less than glowing Criminal Records Bureau background check for the supply agency would now stink a little bit more. My teaching days seemed to be over, at least for now. I was back to the job market trying to convince someone that I could be a decent, reliable employee, despite evidence to the contrary.

To further my anxiety, I received a letter saying that my case would now be referred to the Child Protection Agency. It's odd how, even when you think you can fall no further, there is still a little bit of 'give'. Was there anything else they could do to destroy my name and my prospects? If there was, they were sure to find it. I wrote to an MP who was chairing a committee looking into allegations against teachers. I received no reply, not even an acknowledgement that the receipt of the letter had been logged. If I was in any doubt about the fact that the system for which I had worked had spat me out then that put my mind at rest.

I felt like a non-person, not quite a member of society. I wondered when someone would tell me that I could no longer collect my daughter from school. Maybe I would be allowed to wait outside the school gates for her or enter the premises with an escort. Maybe I would not be permitted any contact with them at all – after all I was a virtual child abuser, was I not? No-one had used that phrase – yet – but what else could it be called? I simply couldn't reconcile my new reality with the facts.

If I were really this person who could not be trusted, this person capable of physical or indecent assault on children, then why was I not languishing in prison? Three children had been harmed or suffered mental distress because of my actions. It was a new truth that I had to accept for the meantime. Facts and evidence didn't come into it. It was an official state of being for me, a documented indictment of David Roy, former teacher. The victors could now write the history books and cast me as whatever monster they chose…and really, I was the worst kind, wasn't I? What sort of man could harm a child?

Someone also told me that with the sort of entry I now had on my CRB that I couldn't emigrate. I had never really considered such a thing but to know that it was now out of the question came as a shock. I was a prisoner in a country that really had nothing for me.

So, my search for a new job continued. I applied to the Royal Mail for a Christmas casual post in the sorting office. They held a recruiting day at Preston North End's football ground. I assumed that there would be thousands of prospective posties there and that we would be sorted out like slaves at market or casual stevedores turning up for a day's work at the docks, but there were actually twelve of us. We were ushered into a side room where we sat at tables in little clutches of four. Our documentation was studied and photocopied while we filled in an application form. I was the first person to finish out of the first intake of the day – a fact which I didn't even think about until much later. I bade my new employers good day and went home to wait for the call. As soon as a position came up I would be contacted.

I didn't hear anything the following week. Nor did I hear anything the week after that. Or the week after that. In fact, I never heard another thing from them. There are two possible reasons for this. One is that they looked at my application, noticed my previous dismissal and decided to give me a wide berth. The other, is that my application being the first of the day to be completed ended up at the bottom of the pile as each successive application was placed on top. As the Christmas rush took hold they worked their way through a pile of candidates and never got to me. Either way my career with Royal Mail was a non-starter. It was another glorious episode in my life. The most disappointing thing was that it was virtually the only job that had even given me a glimpse of hope, only for that to be cruelly taken away.

I found a place on a free course which would enable me to qualify for my SIA licence, which in turn could have led to a thrilling career in retail security. Unfortunately, I was unable to attend the course because I had a job interview, so the world will never know what a great security guard I could have been. The interview in question was actually a two-part affair, the first part being a series of psychometric tests. Success in these might lead to an interview the following day. For once things seemed to be looking up but I knew not to expect too much – there was seemingly no limit to the number of times that fate could kick me while I was down.

In truth the job advert didn't give much away and when I went for the tests I wasn't too sure what I was being tested for other than I might subsequently become an 'Ambulance Crew Member'. Whether this meant taking old people to the clinic to have their ears syringed, or gallantly saving lives with scant regard for my own safety, I knew not.

I was apprehensive but hopeful when I reported to the County Headquarters of St John Ambulance along with two dozen others. I chatted to one prospective candidate, a prison officer ready for a change of career, but before too long we were summoned to a classroom and each allocated a desk. My fellow applicants were a mixed bag, white, Asian, male, female, large and small. One man in particular stood out because of his enormous girth. I knew that he would never make the grade simply because he looked like a medical incident waiting to happen. That may seem like a harsh judgement but certain jobs do not lend themselves to obesity. Mobility and fitness would obviously be important to an ambulance crewmember and that would preclude this particular gent… which just goes to show how wrong you can be, for when I turned up to begin my training on 4th January 2010, he was there. Not only was he there but he was promoted before we had even finished our training the following month!

The psychometric tests included map reading and problem solving. I didn't even get to the end of some of the sections but couldn't gauge how my performance compared to that of the others. I did notice the large gentleman finishing before everyone else and sitting there with a supercilious smile on his face. I instinctively disliked him but wasn't too concerned. Even if I made it through I knew that he wouldn't. The man conducting the tests was a young, ruddy faced youth of great stature and generous waist. He introduced himself, explained what we were doing and what we were hoping to become. All of these details passed me by completely. It transpired that he was my new boss.

Having finished our testing, we were informed that if we were successful we'd receive a telephone call before seven pm inviting us to the interview stage the following day. I didn't think I had done that well in the tests and just had to rely on everyone else doing even worse than me, which didn't feel like a great position to be in. In total they tested about seventy people that day and would invite thirty back the next day to talk their way into just ten places. I tried not to think about it. There was no point in building my hopes up.

As the allotted time limit neared I became tenser and tenser. By six-thirty I thought I might have heard something. I must have stood a chance. Even to have been selected for the testing process felt like progress and having had a hint of success I didn't want to let it slip past me. There was nothing I could do about it but sit and wait. Time marched on and still there was no phone call. Of course, I reasoned, they had more than one phone call to make so perhaps...and then it was seven.

I was every bit as unemployed as I had been this morning, the only difference being the absence of hope. I was so disappointed. After all these months when I couldn't even get a job as a cleaner, I'd had the prospect of a job dangled before my eyes only for it to be snatched away again. Okay so they must have seen something of worth in my CV but that wasn't much use without the job. I didn't get a certificate stating that I had got so far in the selection process for St John Ambulance. I was no further on.

At times like these, drink is not the answer. With that in mind I went to the drinks cupboard and poured myself a generous measure of rum topped off with a stingy measure of coke. I might not have a job but at least I could still blot out the pain of existence with alcohol. Before too long everything would seem right with the world, at least for a short while, and when the buzz wore off I could go to bed. I got an inkling of how proud people descended into drunken despair after losing a job and not finding work again. I wasn't at the point yet but it was there ahead of me like a distant winning post. The rum didn't sully the glass for long so I made another one and sat down to watch Coronation Street, welcoming the chance to watch fictional characters whose fictional lives were more hopeless than my real life. If this all sounds a bit self-pitying then that's probably because I did feel a bit sorry for myself.

I wasn't proud when it came to work. My background was fairly humble in some respects. I'd had a series of so-so jobs until my career peaked as a teacher. If that was my high point then this was my low point. Now I was in a definite trough and the only way was up… but how? I couldn't set my sights any lower and I couldn't set them any higher. Of course, I had my post office job to look forward to but that might not start for weeks – thank God I didn't know then that it would never start.

'Looks like that's it', I said to Diane as the programme's theme music faded.

'Oh well, never mind. Something will turn up', she replied. And then the phone rang.

Chapter Two

A New Start

The next day I awoke, shaved, showered and put on my best suit. I'd stopped drinking the minute I heard the news that I'd been selected for interview and my head was therefore clear. I'd researched St John Ambulance on the internet and read all about its history. As for the rest I would just have to take my chances. One person in three would get the job today. They were taking on ten people and I planned to be one of them. Once again, I made my way down to the crumbling headquarters building and waited in the kitchen/dining room until I was summoned.

Lt Col Julian Crowe OBE, formerly of the Scots Guards, wore a suit which was obviously hand-made and shoes polished to within an inch of their lives. e shook hands and he led me to an office in which I was introduced to another gentleman who would also be interviewing me. This man was Robin Gonard. Colonel Crowe was the Chief Executive Officer and Mr Gonard was the County

Commissioner. Within months of my interview both of them would have left the organisation they represented, perhaps unfairly, under a cloud. Personally, I owed them a debt of gratitude and I am in little doubt that it was Colonel Crowe who ensured that I got a job. It must have been obvious that what he had before him was an old soldier in need of a lift up and that is what I got. I had apparently scored highly enough the previous day to be shortlisted and my responses to the interview questions were also given a score.

'Give me an example of when you can disregard company policy', asked Colonel Crowe.

'Never', I replied and then explained why. I knew straightaway that I had scored points.

'Give me an example of when you have had to work under pressure', asked Mr Gonard. I told him of the time when, as a young soldier in the Gulf, I had to take my Land Rover out into the desert following the outbreak of the war. The only problem was that its alternator was broken and the vehicle wouldn't start. In those early days of what was to be a very short scrap, I think we all believed that we would shortly be operating through a mist of chemical weapons (that is certainly what we were told to expect). Most of us had never been to war – a tour in Northern Ireland didn't count – and this was the unknown.

The only way to get us moving was to find another battery and make a swap. That meant that I had to find another Land Rover and its keys, drive it over to my stricken vehicle, then swap the battery over, before ensuring the donor vehicle could itself be started with its flat battery. This was an arduous, stressful task but our problems weren't over even as we belatedly pulled out through the gates of camp. Without an alternator our battery would run down and eventually the wagon would stop. Not the most elegant solution to an inelegant problem, which didn't seem to please Mr Gonard. Vehicular cannibalism seemed to be frowned upon in the St John's Ambulance Service, but what was said couldn't be unsaid.

'What would you do if you went to a house to collect a patient who was upstairs and the family insisted that you remove your steel toe cap boots, which you are required to wear?', asked Colonel Crowe. I blathered on about negotiating with the family and insisting that we wore our boots but the Colonel cut me short. 'Or you could ring control?', he suggested.

'Yes, obviously I could ring control', I agreed. Perhaps I am reading too much into it but did he want me to get the job and was prepared to give an answer away to boost my score?

Two days later as I left the job centre I got a phone call telling me that I had the job. My outlook on life brightened from that moment on – I had a new career. I was going to be something again. I would pay taxes and contribute to society, all the things I had complained about when I had worked previously. It's only when your self respect is taken from you that you realise what it means to have it. I was never proud of being a teacher but nor was I ashamed of it. In truth the job had an image problem, something which I didn't envisage being the case with my new job. I was going to be an ambulance crewmember, even if I still didn't quite realise what that entailed.

It was the sort of job that no one ever complained about. No one ever said, 'those bloody ambulance crews, sit around all day doing nothing, never turn up when they're supposed to and then two turn up together, never there when you want them and overpaid too.' At least no-one had ever said it to me. Not only could I look forward to this new job but I thought that I might actually be good at it. I wasn't entirely correct about that as it turned out.

Now my fortnightly visits to the job centre took on a new complexion. I wasn't the same as everyone else – I was just biding my time until my new job began early in the new year. It made an astonishing difference to my perspective on life. I had every right to feel bitter about the treatment I had received from the school authorities but had been too concerned with the practicalities of the two hearings I had to attend to feel such strong emotions. As far as I was concerned the fight went on, but in the meantime I had a second chance. Someone, Colonel Crowe to be precise, had put their faith in me, overlooking the superficial difficulties of taking me on. I would make sure that his faith was rewarded.

Christmas was a somewhat less sombre occasion than the previous year's. I was looking forward to starting my training and to meeting my new work colleagues. I put aside my middle-aged sloth and actually relished the challenge that lay ahead. Diane was still consumed with bitterness about our situation – she was bitter enough for two – but I was far more optimistic. One thing had gone right and maybe that heralded a new start for us. I had to hope so anyway. It was my first ever white Christmas and the two girls loved it. Maybe this too was a sign of better things to come.

I pictured myself in my new uniform, behind the wheel of a shiny ambulance, ready to save lives. I was sure I could do the job but probably everyone in the same situation thinks that. I wasn't really too sure what would be involved; I couldn't avoid the conclusion that I was going to be a glorified minibus driver but the training was scheduled to last eight weeks, suggesting a fair degree of medical knowledge being imparted. When I returned to County Headquarters on January 4th I was raring to go.

Our induction concerned the usual housekeeping notes, getting-to-know-you exercises, a quick look around an ambulance and a run through the training programme. The large man I had noticed during the psychometric testing, the one who could never possibly be an ambulance crewmember, was there. He seemed to have a bit of insider knowledge and right from the start presented himself as destined for greatness. His demeanour from my first sight of him suggested that the selection process had been a formality. Had I been a selector, his *exit* from the selection process would have been a formality.

I just didn't like him. 'Never trust anyone whose thighs rub together', had been my watchword for many minutes. When we had been shown round the ambulance I had asked how many stretchers it carried – the answer was one – but I noticed large man smirking and immediately wanted to ask him what the hell he thought was funny. He rubbed me up the wrong way more than any adult I had met for many years.

My other new colleagues were the usual mixed bunch, each with different reasons for being there, different aspirations, different backgrounds and waist measurements, although tending towards the larger end of the girth scale. Half of them had been involved in medical 'activities' before, either as volunteers with St John Ambulance or with Mountain Rescue. The other half, myself included, hadn't and we stayed in these two camps because this factor affected our outlook considerably i.e. some of us didn't think we knew it all and were prepared to learn.

We were paired up with the people who would be our crewmates. The large man was teamed up with a slim attractive young woman, a most unlikely pairing, and I was teamed up with a large-waisted Mancunian bloke with whom I had nothing in common. In fact, the only thing that unified any of us was the fact that we had nothing in common with each other but especially not with our crewmates. This would prove to be an important factor in how we perceived our job in the coming months.

Our first day ended with a child protection lecture. It was all fairly obvious stuff but as we went through the various points I began to wonder how long I was going to last in my new job. I had been completely honest about what had happened to me and had been asked about my dismissal at interview. I explained both the facts and the perceived facts but now as we were told about CRB checks I began to wonder if the Criminal Records Bureau version of events would prove to be my undoing. Would their take on the person I was simply be too much for my new employers? As usual there was nothing I could do about it. I had supplied them with the facts, they had still taken me on, and at least for the meantime I had a job.

On that first day also, we were supplied with our uniform or what parts of it had arrived. I was given two shirts and two pairs of trousers plus a fleece, boots and a high visibility jacket. The green of our uniforms was a much brighter shade of green than the Ambulance Service wore and we would feel rather conspicuous in the coming months once we had completed our training and went out on the road, but a far bigger problem for me was the size of my trousers! I had always been on the slender side, never more so than having lost so much weight recently but these trousers were big enough for me to fit in twice over!

How had this happened I wondered, and then I recalled the circumstances behind my uniform order. I went through the sequence of events. I had been driving home from the job centre when I received the call on my mobile to tell me that I had been successful in getting the job. I had pulled over onto a side street to answer the phone and my new boss went through the fact that I had scored well on the tests and the interview, the start date and such like, before asking me what size I was for the purposes of ordering uniform.

I knew that I took size seven boots so that bit was easy but the rest of it was trickier. I just didn't know what size I was. If I was buying clothes I picked things that looked roughly right and then tried them on without paying much attention to their dimensions; they either fitted or they didn't. We decided between us that my shirts should be small and that my jacket should be a medium but as for my trousers...

'So what waist size do you think you are?', he asked.

'I honestly don't know. I'm quite small', I said.

'So, thirty-eight or forty?'

'I suppose so.'

And that was that. Now I was faced with the enormity (literally) of my trousers. To be quite small in St John Ambulance was to have a thirty-eight-inch waist but what I hadn't known as I spoke in that side street was that I was joining an organisation in which a fifty or sixty-inch waist was not unusual. I tried my uniform on that evening and managed to keep the trousers up with a belt, but the situation was untenable and eventually I bought myself two new pairs that fitted. My wife laughed at me in my uniform which was not the reaction I had been expecting. I had hoped to look heroic rather than comical.

The following day was more of the same at County Headquarters but we were sent home early because of heavy snowfall. The day after that we would move to the ambulance station that would be our base. Our glorious leader had described it in rather glowing terms, telling us about the up-to-date facilities it had. It seemed that he had vision and ambition, that he would be making us into the elite of the private ambulance world and that money would be spent to provide us with the best of everything. I pictured something like Tracey Island from Thunderbirds, complete with a bustling ops. room, buzzing with purposeful energy, a sort of dispatch area with ambulances fuelled up and ready to go. A tannoy would summon the crew to their call and they would sprint out to a vehicle like Battle of Britain fighter pilots on a scramble, getting details from the radio as they started up and performed their final checks. I imagined everything shiny and new, a control tower, garages, glass and chrome, the best of everything....

What I found was a lock-up garage on an industrial estate.

During the night it had filled with water and Rachael, one of my new colleagues, was busy with a large squeegee slopping it out into the drains. There were five vehicles and a wheeled command post, which looked like a converted ISO container, crammed into the tiny space available. One of the vehicles was an old Sherpa ambulance once owned by Florence Nightingale. At the front gate there was an even older ambulance (it might have been a Commer) acting like a gate guardian. In all honesty it looked more like a piece of scrap.

There wasn't even a sign to say that the facility belonged to St John Ambulance. There was an office, a training room, a rest room, a kitchen which was really just a cupboard (and smelt of mouldy rags) and some toilets. Upstairs was an open plan junk room with old-fashioned, obsolete equipment and dress uniforms that seemingly never got worn. It was the sort of stuff that didn't get thrown out 'just in case'. There was probably no one single person who could decide to get rid of it all. I could imagine the sort of process they would go through in assessing what was to be chucked and what was to be kept.

'What about this uniform?', says a large volunteer holding up a Victorian era dress suit.

'No that belongs to Ernest Grimpipe', says another with disdain.

'But he's dead!'

'Well you never know…'

There were books on how to administer first aid in the Georgian era and boxes of things that had never saved any lives and never would. The only thing that could be said in its favour was that it was secure from theft – there was simply nothing that was of any use or value.

The garage was shared with the volunteers, in fact it had been theirs before the advent of Transport Services, the professional branch of St John

Ambulance, to which I now belonged. This would prove to be a source of great friction. In fact, 'conflict' would be a better word for the dramas that would unfold for us all. For now, I was blissfully ignorant of these things.

Our training began in earnest now. For the remainder of our eight weeks we would have our heads filled with clinical facts, learn how to move patients using the various pieces of kit available to us and how to drive the ambulances in a manner that enabled us to take people to hospital without making their condition any worse than it was before they got in.

Initially I enjoyed the training. Having been a biology teacher, the medical terms weren't a complete mystery to me but I began to have my doubts about the training methods employed. Much of it consisted of lectures and 'PowerPoints' with very little practical work to back up our understanding. For instance, later in the course we learned all about delivering a baby. Now, even allowing for the fact this was very much a last resort for us, I did not feel at all confident that I would be able to do it should fate decide that there was no other option. Likewise, the section on 'assisting the paramedic', left me with the distinct impression that the paramedic would be better off without me. Even worse was when our instructor/manager asked us to research a topic and then 'feed back to the rest of the group', which is really just a cop out. The feedback that we got from these sessions was rubbish, a complete waste of time and yet these were things we might really need to know about some day.

The word that we all began to dread was 'scenario'. We would collectively shudder upon hearing it because it meant practising the skills we had learnt. That we should do so was fair enough; the problem lay in the lack of structure these scenarios had. We had been split into two 'watches' and we trained in these groups. Unfortunately for me however the other members of my watch thought that they really didn't have much to learn and that left me floundering for much of the time.

I particularly missed out on learning how to apply the leads for a twelve lead ECG (so called because it had ten leads – I don't understand it either). To ensure that these were applied to the right parts of the chest a bit of rib counting was required. Since I was one of the few trainees whose ribs were actually detectable that meant that I was the one who was practised upon. I never really felt comfortable with using the ECG subsequently, for I had always been the patient rather than the medic during training.

We learned to use a carry chair and a stretcher, and after two weeks we all qualified as Patient Transport Attendants and First Responders. We learned how to use a defibrillator and how to perform basic life support. In time we moved on to retrieving people from cars and how to prioritise treatment. The most involving part was the mass of clinical knowledge we had to accumulate and I spent hours making my own notes and learning medical terms. We were also taught how to use medical gases which sounds more impressive than it is. The two gases at our disposal were oxygen and Entonox, a brand name for 'gas and air'. The latter was for pain relief. I always struggled to work out which mask to use for which type of patient.

The part I enjoyed most was the driver training which lasted two weeks in total but took place on random days of the week. I was teamed up with an ex-policeman called Paul and an ex-cabin attendant named Rachael, both of whom remained my friends in the forthcoming months. Our instructor Brendan was an ex-fire officer and under his tutelage we tore round the Lancashire countryside in our unwieldy Renault ambulances. It was often hair-raising stuff.

Particularly buttock-clenching was our night drive in Wales; I vividly remember racing along narrow country roads in the pitch black, using all of the road where possible and far exceeding the speed limit. The night was a cold blur of blacks and greys as we hurtled along.

About halfway through out drive we stopped off for chips and sat in the back of the ambulance chatting for a while, a surreal situation but one full of comradeship. Had I only ever had to work with these three, life would have been grand.

As the end of our training approached the final pieces of documentation that we required to carry out our jobs – medical clearance and CRBs – came through in dribs and drabs. With regard to the former I was a drib but for the latter I was very much a drab. In fact, I was the drabbiest drab there was. Everyone else had received their CRBs but I, ominously the only person expecting to have an entry on theirs, was kept waiting until the penultimate week. The boss man had been looking at me as if to say, 'you're not going to make the grade' and he was expecting to find himself a man down once I was ejected.

When the envelope arrived, I opened it with trepidation. I dreaded what it might have written in it and pictured myself having to say goodbye to my new colleagues. I tore the envelope open, my mouth dry. The folded sheet slipped out and I laid it out flat like an old-fashioned proclamation. There were no adverse entries on it at all. I checked again. There was nothing to say what a bad person I was, nothing whatsoever detrimental. I could scarcely believe it. To ensure that I kept my new job, I had even been in touch with the person who would eventually represent me at tribunal to vouch for me and got a copy of my old CRB from the supply agency.

Now I had a spanking new CRB which left me totally in the clear. I remembered now the threat to inform the Child Protection Agency of my case – I had never heard another thing from them.

Our final week saw our assessment day and we worked our way through written papers and the dreaded scenarios. I scraped through the first one, a woman with a heart problem, which I failed to diagnose but managed to treat the symptoms. I failed the second one which was supposed to be a trauma casualty but in fact had hypothermia. Knowing that this was my trauma scenario blinded me to my casualty's main complaint – something which would not happen in real life. I was so determined to find bleeding or a break that I ignored their dangerously low temperature. I realised that they needed to be warmed but to have covered them in a blanket would have prevented me from properly assessing their injuries. It was a bit unfair. I messed up my resuscitation scenario because we were pretending to be in a moving vehicle and I didn't tell the driver to stop. Also, the valve in the bag valve mask was in back to front so the equipment didn't actually work properly. I scraped through the written exam.

All in all, it was a poor performance. Never in my life had I been quite so bad at anything. Ironically, I was the first person to qualify as an Advanced Emergency Transport Attendant, simply because I went through my scenarios just slightly ahead of anyone else. I was glad it was over but I really couldn't work up any enthusiasm for my new job; my confidence was low.

Chapter Three

Preparation for Tribunal

The name on the piece of paper given to me by my former colleague as I waited to go into the Appeal was that of Jenni Watson. Of course, I had no idea who she was, but I rang her and explained my situation. Jenni was a former deputy headteacher who now acted as an advocate for sacked teachers. She was kept busy. Quite how I would have proceeded had her name not been given to me I don't know but she made the difference between success and failure. I put my fate into her hands and let her get on with it.

I had already got things underway with the tribunal by completing their paperwork online but I was acting alone then and quite unsure if I was going about it the correct way. It was a relief when they told me that my claim had been accepted; in effect that I would have a hearing even though it was months away. I gave Jenni a précis of the events that had gone before, copies of all the papers and documents I had received and details of the ET1 form I had completed for the Tribunal Service. In return I signed an agreement to co-operate with her and that I undertook to meet the costs incurred.

Jenni's services didn't come cheaply although she charged a lot less than a solicitor. However it was money well spent – in excess of £20,000 as it transpired. Had I not had access to this sum I would have probably spent the rest of my life being the new character that Fennel and her pals had created for me.

The union had given up on me, stating that they didn't think my case was winnable. This really grated. I had spent a small fortune on fees over the years and never really got a lot in return. Martin Fisher had given me his reasons why he didn't think the union would continue with its support but suggested that I apply for their assistance anyway. The rejection letter I received back was a rehash of Martin's reasoning – clearly, he had been consulted on the decision and his ideas recycled. I had just wasted my time in applying. Even after successfully winning my tribunal months later they refused to concede that the case had been eminently winnable and that they had made a mistake. I never did get that money back.

Jenni, on the other hand, told me that she thought that the case could be won and that she would take over responsibility for my fight back. She encouraged me to check my house insurance to see if it included legal cover. It didn't, of course, because I thought that I would never need it. I checked my car insurance as well but there was nothing. I would be stumping up the cost myself. I had money put aside for... well not for this, but money is money. We established that my tribunal would be held in April and four days were allocated to hear evidence and reach a verdict. Jenni made contact with my witnesses and the relevant documents changed hands.

As we closed in on the date of tribunal our email correspondence increased as the case was built. She was particularly interested in the personalities of the people she faced, trying to understand them, their strengths and weaknesses. Each one became a target for her and she compiled a daunting portfolio of questions that they would face in court. Her plans were meticulous, with absolutely nothing left to chance. Perhaps we could have won with five or ten questions per witness but Jenni would have fifty or a hundred in readiness.

We finally met in early April when Diane and I were staying in York. I made the journey over to her house in Humberside and we chatted about the direction the case was heading and what I could expect when faced with the panel of judges and my tormentors. Jenni was a distinguished, no-nonsense lady, forthright and immensely capable. I recognised at once that she was a good ally and a formidable foe; I was glad that to me she was the former..

She made it clear that she was taking nothing for granted. No matter how unfair *I* thought my dismissal was, it would still be necessary to make sure that the judges agreed. It all came down to putting on the right show and appearing to be credible. The tribunal was not a 'retrial' but rather an examination of the way in which the original investigation and hearings had been carried out. My opponents only had to prove that they had acted in a reasonable manner with regards to the information given to them. If they had made the wrong decision for the right reasons then theoretically at least they were partly in the clear.

Equally, I could actually win my case by proving that the investigation had been wrongly carried out, even if there remained a suspicion of my guilt. To win in this way would have been unsatisfactory for me; I was innocent and wanted that to be made clear. I didn't want to get away with it on a technicality. That's not to say that their incompetence didn't play a part in the final verdict – it shone through like a beacon of idiocy – but I wanted the whole thing, the strongest judgement that could be made in my favour. This wasn't mere emotional greed on my part, it was my name at stake – in fact it felt like my whole life was at stake and meaningless without the appropriate judgement. I simply had to stop being that person they said I was. For it to be otherwise would be a lingering punishment for my children and my wife. I had to prove that there could be smoke without fire. I needed someone to expose the conspiracy for me – I could never do it for myself. That person was Jenni.

Almost on a whim I suggested that I contact Allyson England the other witness to the incident with John. Her testimony had not been strong in its delivery, even if the words, viewed on paper, seemed very damning. It was clear that her heart wasn't in it. What prompted this tentative idea was that redundancies had been announced at the school and Allyson was one of about a dozen casualties. I was loath to take advantage of her bad news but equally this might be an opportunity to get her on my side. This, I thought, would be like the final nail in the coffin for the case against me, although Jenni was more circumspect. She knew that we still had a small mountain to climb even with every advantage. It was obvious that our opponents would try to discredit Sara and Allyson if the latter chose to change her allegiance.

They could say that they were only changing sides because they had no connection to the school anymore and that they would not have done so had they still been employed there. The opposite view could be taken, that freed from the constraints of that particular employer they were able to speak the truth.

Nothing ventured, nothing gained as they say in cliché-land. I made contact through Sara (they remained friends) and the idea was put to her. In a sense she had nothing to lose but there was still that residual fear of her former boss to overcome. Both she and Sara found Fennel intimidating. I never had. I found her loathsome, weak and not terribly bright but I was never afraid of her. In my opinion she was a completely hopeless human being who could do nothing without resorting to deceit. She'd had her way for too long but things were different now. Her stock was low. It was rumoured that she had lost her new advisory job in line with the general trend for public sector redundancies. The truth of this was difficult to ascertain but either way I wasn't ready to shed a tear.

The gamble paid off. With just a hint of reluctance Allyson agreed and I passed her details to Jenni. As far as I was concerned, that was it for the opposition: their case was untenable. That was only my opinion. Nothing was guaranteed.

We all qualified as ambulance crew at the end of February and began helping out with the Ambulance Service the following month. We put out three ambulances a day on ten-hour shifts, gaining valuable experience of our new jobs. Mainly we did what were called, 'doctor's urgents', in which a GP had been summoned to a household and decided that the patient therein needed hospital treatment. 'Urgent' was a bit of a misnomer, as our patients could be waiting for hours before we were even given the job of collecting them.

Occasionally they vented their spleen, blaming us for the delay, but mostly the people were very nice, calm and helpful. Some of them were very ill indeed but without immediately life-threatening conditions. They had every right to be bitter about the hand that fate had dealt them, but this was rarely the case. Having been a teacher for so many years where it seemed as if every minor inconvenience turned into a major incident (for some children, at least) it was extremely refreshing to meet people who were glad to see me, took my advice, accepted my help and did their best to get on with things. The absence of complaint was astonishing. One disturbing tendency made itself known at this early stage: that of staff trying to upgrade the calls we were on.

The ambulance service was using us almost exclusively for doctor's urgents, hospital transfers and discharges. They were glad of our help because it freed up their own crews for more of the emergency type work they needed to do. Unfortunately, having been trained to do some aspects of this emergency work ourselves, some crew members were exaggerating the seriousness of some of the jobs they were given. On occasions crews ran on blue lights, when in fact they weren't allowed to. Sometimes we transported patients who should have been taken by more highly qualified medics. The lustre of my new job began to wear off quickly because I was in no mood to take work for which we weren't adequately trained.

The ambulance service control had it about right with the tasks they gave us. If a patient deteriorated significantly on the way to hospital then I had no problem with contacting control, explaining this and asking if we could proceed on blues, but other than that it was a case of 'count me out'. I was trying to dig my way out of one pile of manure without having more of the stuff dumped on me. There would be no hiding place, no justification, no back-up, if one of us crashed when we were on lights and sirens without permission and both crewmembers would be called to account, not just the driver.

At the end of March 2010, our temporary contract with the ambulance service ended abruptly. Our work dried up almost completely and we were faced with the prospect of losing our jobs if Transport Services began operating at a loss. April was spent in enforced idleness, moping around the garage, cleaning ambulances until they gleamed with sterility, and generally grouching. With my tribunal looming I became introverted and morose. These forthcoming events would decide how I lived the rest of my life; in everlasting shame or as a normal person. It was an almost unbearable burden at times, especially when I had nothing to take my mind off it. It was a gloomy period for me.

To break the monotony and try to bag some contracts we were often dispatched to various local hospitals to drive round and be noticed. I seriously doubt if this did any good but it got us out of the garage at least. The day before my tribunal was due to start I was sent to Manchester St John Ambulance to collect an orthopaedic mattress needed for a job. On the return leg of my journey I drove past the tribunal buildings and also located the nearest train station. That night I pressed my boots and polished my suit. I was ready.

There was much uncertainty about the outcome for the reasons already given but at least I was now taking the fight to my former employers. For the first time I wasn't playing a passive role and it was for them to justify the decision they had taken to sack me. There was no doubt in my mind that they had received an unpleasant shock when the letter from the Tribunal Service fell onto their mat. This was all extremely inconvenient and potentially expensive for them and I hoped that they now began to appreciate the enormity of the mistake they had made.

Surely, they realised that by taking this action I really believed in my innocence. Based on their previous experience of such matters, I should have just given up by now and accepted my fate. I hope that they were worried. The affair was now being looked at by independent people, not Blackpool LEA cronies. My opponents could bring no influence to bear and this was no longer a formality for them.

The train journey to Manchester gave me plenty of time to consider the facts of the case again, to think about what had been done to me. I still kept bitterness or anger at bay, maintaining my focus on the outcome I needed. This was a job of work, not some mental exercise. I needed restraint, economy of emotion, clarity of thought.

I established the whereabouts of the Tribunal Service building and made my way to Costa for a pick-me-up coffee. Ever the pragmatist, I opted for an espresso on the assumption that this would require fewer subsequent trips to the toilet. I wasn't actually keen on it but you can't have everything; this was no pleasure cruise. The trip to Costa became a morning routine and I took the time to look at my fellow customers and wonder what their stories were. What sort of day had they in prospect? Would it be better or worse than mine?

I met Jenni in the claimant's waiting room. I was a piece of flotsam in a small sea of hopefuls, all seeking justice for dismissals they deemed to be unfair. Any cheer was of the forced variety, for the most part people were glum and reticent, which was fine by me, I wasn't planning on striking up any new friendships. Most of these people would be present for one day only, but not Jenni and me. She arrived shortly before we were due to start and then after completing a few forms we were led down the corridor to the room in which the hearing would be held.

At this point I was reacquainted with Fennel, Gee, Neath and Wenman and a few pleasantries were exchanged through gritted teeth. Fennel was determined to appear to be the voice of reason, its very personification, in fact. She looked haggard, almost shrunken, as if her recent trials had taken their toll on her. She had failed miserably at the only thing that mattered to her and her humiliation was not yet complete. She had ruined my professional life but I still felt as if I was much more fortunate than her. When I counted my blessings, I had a wife who stood by me and loved me, and two beautiful children. She couldn't do anything to change that. She had none of the things which made my life worthwhile. I would be lying if I said that I felt any compassion for her but nor was I in a position to gloat.

Chapter Four

The Topic of Cancer

By now I had other worries. To be sitting in that little room, virtually on trial again, with my professional future ready to be reclaimed or dispatched forever was bad enough, but now I had to contend with the likelihood that my wife had cancer.

'I've got a lump on my neck', she said one day as I returned from work. I looked and on her left shoulder, where it joined the neck and just above her clavicle there was what appeared to be a swelling. It was not discoloured but it was there for sure. 'I don't want to die', she said and dissolved in tears. What do you do? I held her close and assured her that everything would be okay. Even with my eight weeks of ambulance training behind me I couldn't say this with any certainty but what else was there for me to say?

I was sufficiently naïve to expect that my misfortunes would come to me over a long period of time, spread out and issued in easily-dealt-with little packets. Instead it appeared that I had two major problems running concurrently. Either would have been quite enough for me. I can't claim to be overly resilient or to enjoy a surfeit of stoicism, but I had no option but to carry on. No doubt things could have been worse, but it was hard to imagine that being the case. Examples of things that *are* worse are too terrible to contemplate. I confess to feeling rather put upon at that time.

A trip to the GP confirmed that there was something amiss and an appointment was made for Diane to see a consultant. I always thought that if either of us got cancer it would be me – in fact I did actually think that I'd had it the previous year, when upon returning from a run I found blood in my urine. I was alarmed and immediately assumed the worst, although in fairness the various doctors I saw seemed to assume the worst also. Before long I was being subjected to a series of tests that came in rapid succession, some of which were rather uncomfortable shall we say. Uncomfortable in this instance is a euphemism. After a number of weeks, it was decided that the bleeding was the result of the running rather than cancer. When I ran my bladder bruised and I bled. I had so many other things to worry about at the time that I rarely even thought about my medical problem.

Diane visited a consultant who didn't mention cancer but hinted that she might well be seriously ill. The manner of his speech and the things he *didn't* say immediately alerted me to cancer and when I checked out the symptoms on the internet it pointed to Hodgkin's Lymphoma, information which I didn't share with Diane. He had hinted that it might be TB but I could tell that he didn't really believe this. Our next trip to see him confirmed my e-diagnosis.

Life changed for us again; we now had a seriously ill person in the house. My tenet was 'business as usual', which was easy for me to say – I didn't have the cancer. Diane's treatment would be gruelling and take many months but the prognosis was good. Most people survived and led normal lives afterwards simply because the chemotherapy regime had been refined to such an extent that it worked in ninety-five per cent of cases. I did give myself a nasty shock during my initial internet research of the subject when I discovered that all the statistics relating to Hodgkin's Lymphoma related to people surviving for five years. Five years! Only five years! I was crushed... until I read that they meant that after five years they stopped monitoring the patient, not that the patient expired.

My wife now had to 'battle' cancer but of course she did no such thing because it is impossible to battle cancer. Instead you put yourself in the hands of the NHS, they treat you, and you hope for the best. It is an entirely passive experience where your only hope lies in the effect of the various toxic chemicals pumped into your veins. There was precious little else to do except put up with it. By the time my tribunal began I knew she had cancer, but she didn't. In May the precise situation became clear to us and the treatment started shortly after that. It is hard to avoid thinking dark thoughts at times like this. Neither of us had exactly been floating on air for some time but this was just another cruel blow. We desperately needed some good news but we would have to wait.

Once Diane's treatment began in earnest I felt like my entire life was spent at hospitals. At work I was visiting Lancaster, Blackburn, Burnley and Preston hospitals, and several more in equally exotic locations. On many of my days off, I was taking Diane to Preston for her chemo. Things improved to some extent when it became clear that the treatment was working, but the effects became progressively more debilitating with each session. Diane's hair thinned and then fell out and she spent more and more time in bed just exhausted. On occasions she almost slept round the clock. She was exhausted, and so was I.

Chapter Five

Turning the Tide

The witnesses came up in a preordained order, but a special dispensation was made for Mr Wenman, a nurse who could only get one day off from his vital work. Dressed in what looked like a brand-new suit and ear-ring, Wenman clearly thought he looked the very essence of sophisticated cool. But there is some indefinable quality bestowed upon the wearer of a suit. I'm not sure if it stems from the suit itself or something else but some men wear suits and look like gentlemen, whilst others merely look like footballers. Wenman's suit had a spivish quality to it. He looked like a brainless thug dressed as a diplomat, or how a brainless thug would expect a diplomat to dress. I could picture him standing for hours in front of a mirror looking at his new threads, acting out his big moment in court, and yet all the care and attention he could lavish upon himself changed nothing. Some men could wear a cheap suit and make it look expensive but he did the exact opposite.

He took the stand which in reality meant that he sat behind a desk and was asked to read out an oath. He was in combative mood, ready for anything, his razor-sharp mind primed for action. I was reminded of a weasel.

In my limited experience, court rooms are nowhere near as grand as you expect them to be and this was even less grand than that. It was a room, and nothing more. It had less character than a doctor's waiting room. On a raised dais there sat a long table and in front of that a set of tables at which Jenni and I would sit. Next to us would be the barrister representing the school. At right angles to that was a single desk at which the person giving evidence sat. Behind us there were rows of seats for witnesses, well-wishers, the press and fans of employment tribunals. Each judge had two huge bundles of notes, as did the witness.

The three judges were all in their late fifties or early sixties. In the centre was Judge Russell, who was *de facto* leader of the panel. He was not required to wear a wig but presumably he had been a barrister or judge prior to his time with the Employment Tribunal Service. By the sound of his voice, I imagined he was drawn from the top echelons of society, educated at the best schools and universities, familiar with good tailoring, and at ease in social functions.

To his left as we faced them was another gentleman who I later discovered had a trades union background. Within the strictures of professional inscrutability, he seemed the most affable of the three, often seen hiding a wry smile behind his hand as proceedings got underway. He was heavily built; the sort of man who might have played rugby in his youth. To Judge Russell's right was a female panellist, and her background was that of employer. She was the most inscrutable of the three but seemed stern and business-like. She listened intently to all that was said, only her follow-up questions giving any indication of the thoughts generated by proceedings.

All three took copious notes and asked pointed questions which gave an insight to the conclusions they were reaching. I was encouraged by their obvious attention to detail and the interest which they displayed; my hearing was not a formality – they were set upon the pursuit of truth and justice. Broadly speaking, Judge Russell seemed to favour the school initially, the other male judge seemed to be coming down on my side, and the female judge seemed to be maintaining a readily discernible even-handedness. I became an avid watcher of their body language, trying to gain an insight into their minds' workings. Maybe I saw what I wanted to see, but by the end of the first day it would be fair to say that the integrity of the case against me and of the people who had created it was severely in doubt.

I made hasty notes in my own indecipherable shorthand, for no other reason than because Jenni had asked. I recently lost the notebook in which they were written so the following account can only be taken as an approximation of what was said. In fact, it is the highlights of that approximation that nevertheless give an idea about the flavour of the hearing.

On the first day we had Fennel and Wenman sworn in. The former was there to salvage her reputation as much as I was. I still couldn't escape the conclusion that her downfall, if not precipitated by her handling of my case, was more easily achieved as a result of it.

She was here as the *former* head of the school, and even if the judges considered this to be an irrelevance to the actual case, it must have been embarrassing for her to relive those times before she was removed. Her ability to conduct a fair investigation may have been in doubt simply because her removal from the headship implied doubt about her abilities generally. The judges knew that she had lost her job for whatever reason and this fact could only have influenced the opinion they formed of her, even as they steadfastly maintained their impartiality. They could hardly have failed to register the irony either.

Jenni began her questioning and made Fennel look at her reasons for recommending my dismissal.

She asked if it was fair that the first case was included in the list of allegations when in fact I was being tried twice. She alluded to the fact that Fennel was a JP and asked if she would be happy to try someone twice for the same crime. She asked why I had not been asked to make statements and why the procedure for taking statements had not been followed. Jenni went into detail about the wording of the charges, pointing out that they changed seemingly on a whim. She tried to draw Fennel out about her reliance upon the word of the mysterious Kate Ryding and about the fact that teachers were allowed to restrain children in certain circumstances; it was not enough for Fennel to say that teachers couldn't do it, when the government's view was that they could. She asked why the doctor's reports that they requested were disregarded. She asked about the Pygmalion report which backed up the views expressed by me at the meeting in the previous March but which had been strongly refuted by Fennel. Jenni painted a picture – an accurate one – of a teacher struggling to maintain order in a school in terminal decline. The following passage is reproduced *exactly* as written by its author, my representative Jenni Watson. It was these questions that she used in defence of my good name, or to vanquish my foes if you prefer. The page and paragraph numbers refer to documents that could be checked by the judges as we went through.

NOT AN INVESTIGATION BUT THE CREATION OF A CASE

Your job as an investigator was to ascertain facts – yes?

In respect of Jack why did you not ask - at any time - any of the many witnesses of any incident (pupils, dinner ladies, staff on duty) in the school hall what they had seen?

*Ms Maddox and Ms England did not see any part of the originating incident with John *******. Why did you not ask questions of any of the witnessing children in the classroom?*

Did you do any further investigation at all of the Debbie matter after you brought it back into the frame as an allegation?

Why is there no account of the incident written by John himself? ·

Why is there no personal account of the incident written by Jim himself?

Why did you not interview Jim in January?

Why did you not interview Mrs Summerlee in January?

Why did you tell Mr Roy the investigation was complete in January? (minutes of suspension meeting on 8th Jan at 77)

You obviously considered you had enough information in January 2009 for something without doing these things - what was it?

In effect you thought you had enough proof of Mr Roy's guilt to persuade a panel of it without enquiring further? (Go to 208 for what she says!)

You say in your statement at para 10 that you were entitled to re-open the case Mrs Summerlee had dealt with because she didn't have the authority to investigate and resolve it. And in para 13 you say you did re-open it on 31st March. Rubbish - knew about that on 17th December, then told him investigation was complete in January.

No mention to anyone inc strategy meetings about 'opening it again' It is ex post-facto rationalisation Ms Fennel. – designed to get you off the hook of dealing with yet ANOTHER incident TWICE, isn't it?

....

LET'S SEE JUST HOW YOU INVESTIGATED

You did various interviews between January and June?

Is it a fair summary of those months to say you interpreted the material you had in early January 2009 in a particular way (i.e. that Mr Roy had three times assaulted pupils) and after coming to that conclusion nothing Mr Roy said in the following months made you disbelieve that?

You operated from the premise that Mr Roy was guilty unless he could prove himself innocent, didn't you?

Why did you not allow witnesses to write their own statements and give them to you, signed?

You didn't follow the disciplinary procedure in respect to that at all did you?

Your so-called statements are very short. Why is that?

You only wanted certain elements of what the witnesses might have told you, didn't you?

The interviews done after the investigation meetings with Mr Roy were to clarify very specific issues weren't they? They were hardly full scale investigations of all the facts were they?

Why did you tell Mr Roy that the investigation had been completed and then write telling him you were beginning another one? (see 359)

You had decided a long time before that Mr Roy was not fit to teach children and should be dismissed if OHP could not provide a medical get-out, hadn't you? (see strategy minutes 308, 321, 343)

See page 178 – You explain here, don't you, why further witness statements were taken? "because Mr Roy changed his version of accounts." Not because you wanted a wider picture?

And 92 (a) you say the same.

See page 41: Your interviews with Mr Dodd and Mrs Summerlee on 12th and 15th June 2009 were after the decision to follow up your accusation of gross misconduct with a move to a recommendation of governors to dismiss, weren't they?

You had already told the strategy meeting on the 11th (343/343) what you were doing. These two interviews weren't investigation but preparation of your case against Mr Roy.

You had actually been preparing a case against Mr Roy since 8th January, hadn't you?

See page 39: <u>You</u> were the person making the allegation of gross misconduct on 8th January, weren't you? (note suspension letter at 78) Somebody had to have decided by then to see the three incidents as belonging together and to have interpreted them as potential gross misconduct (hence the suspension) who was the originator of that idea?

Miss Gee had made the decision to suspend the day before at the strategy meeting, hadn't she? (308) Miss Gee has no power to suspend does she? She told you to do it and you did, the following day, yes? (proof in OH referral at 79

Right — so we had the allegation of inappropriate physical intervention created at the strategy meeting on 7th. Who decided by 8th January that such an allegation equated to gross misconduct?

It matters. I want to know which of you made this important decision, and why?

GROSS MISCONDUCT

See page 78 – where did your allegation of gross misconduct come from? 'inappropriate physical intervention ' - You say it is in accordance with the disc procedure. Look at it – 254. (physical violence) who changed it?

Do you really think you have a right to misquote a contractual procedure in that manner? The procedure does not say what you suggest it says, does it?

After Mr Roy had been sacked, in September 2009, you published what you should have had in place before that – a Physical Intervention Policy. Please look at it on page 360. Physical intervention is <u>not</u> gross misconduct, is it?

Mr Roy had a pupil behaving in a way that compromised good order. He had to act immediately when the pupil pushed him out of his way. He had the right to use reasonable force, didn't he?

So as early as 8th January (page 78) you were planning disciplinary action on a piece of procedure you had twisted.

....

TWO INCIDENTS HAD ALREADY BEEN DEALT WITH

Do you accept that the Debbie incident had been investigated fully by way of a Child Protection process, and then –internally – by your deputy, in September 2008 and determined in a disciplinary process to have exonerated Mr Roy - effectively regarding it as an accident and not an assault? (Go to 57)

Do you accept that a senior member of staff had dealt with the Jim incident to her, the parent and the child's satisfaction on 2nd and 3rd December 2008? (Go to 52)

Do you accept that Mrs Summerlee, with training in all your procedures did not see this as an assault or even see a need to report this matter to you as a disciplinary incident at the beginning of December, [remember the email of late March '09 when she was still of the same opinion 170]

Neither of these families saw any reason to believe their youngsters had been abused by Mr Roy, did they?

And in fact neither Mrs Summerlee nor Jim wanted to pursue any external process either, did they?

Do you accept there were no outstanding complaints from any of the three children in January 2009 and they had all been dealt with? See bottom of 313

There was nothing Mrs Summerlee and John were waiting for, was there? So all three incidents had been dealt with?

Well you didn't tell any of these families that you were seeking Mr Roy's dismissal because of his actions towards their children, did you?

NECESSITY FOR CONSIDERATION OF S550A

The allegation on page 39 was what you were investigating, and the questions you had to research the facts for were focused on appropriateness - the nature extent and reasons for physical intervention - if it happened.

521 need at strategy meeting to consider s550A – the idea was never mentioned at any strategy meeting was it?

Government advice clearly sets out circumstances where physical intervention is permitted. You did not examine any of the pupil's behaviour from this point of view at all, did you?

Look at doc. at 480

Yet this is 'taking into account the pupil's behaviour' is just what you did when you exonerated Mr Roy of any blame over Debbie, isn't it?

You effectively deemed it an accident for which Mr Roy could not be held to blame, didn't you?

Why did you not 'take into account the pupil's behaviour' when examining the John issue?

Look at the policy you brought in the September after this event (policy 52) page 360.

Why did John not do the detention he skipped?

You didn't examine his behaviour at all, did you? Either at the time or later?

You obviously then considered that a pupil could do anything he liked but it did not justify any physical response from the teacher?

But you didn't ask him - or anybody else - any questions about the behaviour that began this incident, did you?

....

IT WAS AN INTERNAL MATTER, NOT SAFEGUARDING + FENNEL SHOULD NOT HAVE INVESTIGATED

By the time of the first strategy meeting you already knew that the Police did not wish to bring any sort of case, didn't you?

And that Social Services saw no concern for their involvement?

So at that point the Child Protection questions had been answered and the matter was an internal one for the school - yes?

The internal process was not within any safeguarding procedures, but a straight conduct or capability matter - yes?

But you believed, right from the beginning, that Mr Roy was not a fit person to teach, didn't you? (agreed at strategy meetings)

How could you do a fair and objective investigation?

It was you making the allegation. How could you fairly investigate it?

USE OF OHP RATHER THAN PYGMALION FACTS

Why was Mr Roy referred to OHP?

See 79 The decision has already been made that Mr Roy is guilty of inappropriate physical intervention . It is stated as a fact – the very allegation he was eventually dismissed for.

See 81 – you want to know if medical redeployment can be recommended. You say the investigation has already been completed and you await the report from OHP to give an indication of the way to proceed with the matter.

One way or another, by way of medical intervention if possible, Mr Roy was to be removed from post, wasn't he? [she didn't disagree with any strategy minutes]

Because he said he could not cope / teach/ do his job properly because of the unremedied behaviour of the pupils - rather than admit he was describing what all teachers had major concerns about - you decided he was mentally ill.

165 and 164 at * *This is the government telling you what teachers have a right to expect, isn't it ?*

Pygmalion Report at 462 and Section 4. (474) This was the context for Mr Roy's views wasn't it ? He was one of the teachers whose morale was reduced in the way the report describes. Why is there no mention at all of this factor in your investigation report?

And you tried to ignore it. We asked for minutes of meetings where the Pygmalion report was discussed by governors. There aren't any. Why not?

See 364: September 2009 This is the only reference. You didn't give the governors the report or the truth, did you?

Was your response to this report to leave the school mid-term without the statutory notice period?

PERSONAL ANIMUS –V- GOOD TRACK RECORD

You were against him right from the very first strategy meeting, weren't you? See 307 onwards

This was a teacher who you had never put into any form of capability procedure for lack of competence, yes?

Look at page 283 - 292 and then 316. You had twice given him temporary promotions.

Look at page 283 - 292 and then 316. you had twice given him temporary promotion during staff absences, and you had adjudged him twice as making sustained and substantial progress by putting him through the teacher's pay threshold to the upper pay scale, and within that, two years later, lifting him from point 2 to point 3. This picture is far from the picture you painted to the strategy meeting isn't it? 309 "He's had support from a number of people and they all had concerns. There is only so much you can do to support someone."

You say that in the strategy meeting but make no mention of all these people or their concerns in the disciplinary hearing, did you?

And there is no mention of any such interventions, or reports of their concerns in Mr Roy's personal file are there?

The elevation from upper pay scale 2 to 3 (page 316) came AFTER incident number 1, didn't it?

. . . .

IMPROPRIETY AT APPEAL STAGE

You brought no witnesses to the disc. hearing but 4 witnesses to the appeal. Since this was a hearing to decide whether the decision of the first panel was fairly taken on the evidence they had at the time, why did you bring them?

And you primed them first with what you wanted them to say, didn't you?

Look at 195 - questions for M Dodd - what is the text below those questions?

Look at 193,197 and 199 - sets of questions with text. The text is what you expected them to say, isn't it?

And the questions themselves - an attempt to produce new evidence?

See 193 - what previous incident were you trying to bring out at this late stage Ms Fennel?

You were very frightened that Mr Roy's appeal might succeed, weren't you?

Debbie's incident was not a child protection matter - that was settled as being an accident - it was an internal conduct matter wasn't it? The statutory agencies had declined to pursue it. Mr Lea's task was as at 514 - AFTER child protection questions had been resolved, wasn't it ?

Look at your response to Mr Roy's appeal grounds. 178 Did you put this in front of the appeal panel?

Your response to the first ground of appeal. You rely for your assertion about "such incidents" on the particular page of a document. Did you produce it to the panel? So they only had your word?

Look at page 536 - halfway down. <u>This</u> is page 241 of the 2006 version of Working Together – the government's generic inter-agency advice following the Victoria Climbie *report. Where does it say that any incident can be brought to any subsequent safe-guarding related disciplinaries?*

You misled the governors about a very important matter, didn't you?

Now compare 536 with 201-202 (part of a later version of the same document as 178) Does the government's document say "not just for 'reference' purposes"? NO

Can you explain why?

Look at what you tell the panel about Kate Ryding. Was she present as a witness? Did she hear the case? Did Mr Roy have the opportunity of putting any evidence to her?

When she says "It is clear that….. he is unsuitable to work with children." that is an opinion based on objective research is it? - but you relied on it to sway the governors, didn't you? See 214 (summation)

Go back to the re-worked document at 201 to page 204. Compare Braund with page 181. You have deliberately taken out the information that this document wasn't received until AFTER the suspension and that Mr Roy had had no opportunity to address it, haven't you?

Look at the new addition for the appeal panel: "I can confirm…" You can't confirm anything of the sort. You weren't on the panel. You were trying to use your position as the head with these governors to get what you wanted: i.e. "I – your head – can confirm."

Bottom para of 204 – the head again.

See 205 - comparing appeal ground 8 with the one on 182, we see that you have added, as a riposte to Mr Roy's request for clemency, a reference to the disciplinary procedure. It is at 254 We have already looked at it. Initially you quoted it as saying "physical intervention" now it has become : 'physical behaviour.' The procedure you are supposedly asking the panel to rely on says 'physical violence'. That is deceit, Ms Fennel, isn't it?

And you tell them that the dismissing panel relied on three incidents. You had no idea about what they relied on because they told no-one.

Nor had you any idea as to whether the panel saw all three incidents as evidence of the same factor, had you?

Para 27 of your statement You are not the headteacher and you no longer hold any statutory powers or duties. It is not proper for you to speak for the school in this way, is it?

Fennel had no viable answers to anything she was asked.

She began confidently enough but before too long was floundering and making unconvincing statements that made her judgement seem poor. Soon she had exhausted her defence and barely responded to Jenni's questions at all. She couldn't explain why no statements had been sought from me other than that in the second case I had already admitted to my guilt. There was absolutely no evidence of me having done so at all. It was obvious that the investigation was completely skewed in favour of the children and that I had had almost no opportunities to defend myself at all. Finally, as the coup de grace, Jenni referred to Fennel's recently produced statement for the tribunal in which she claimed that as headteacher of the school she had no option but to prevent me working there.

'But you're not the headteacher any more, are you Ms Fennel?', she asked. There followed a brief but profound silence which underlined the importance of Fennel's response. The judges looked on intently as if this were the moment when justice hung demonstrably in the balance.

'No, I'm not', she replied quietly. This held the key not only to her personality but to her state of mind. She had sought to portray me as a dangerous loon, only to expose herself as someone whose grip on reality was dubious. In those few words she betrayed herself; she had not let go of the school even if it had let go of her. Had she ever been the right person to pursue the case against me?

That she had been badly advised was not in doubt and became ever clearer as the days went by, but it was also clear that there was a malicious element to her actions and that she didn't fully understand the legislation she relied upon. It got worse for her. The only slight problem was the attitude of Judge Russell. Jenni had scored point after point from Fennel and not one of the latter's rejoinders had made any impact or sounded remotely plausible, fair or sensible... and yet the judge's interjections sounded very much as if he were favouring Fennel. No, perhaps that isn't quite right. More accurately he was at odds with Jenni over some of the things she said and was giving Fennel a way out, an escape from some of the questions. It was as if he had some sympathy for the latter, even if nothing she said was actually defensible.

The other two judges seemed to be in our favour. Jenni had exposed Fennel's reasoning as idiotic, her grasp on procedure and fairness slight. The male panellist seemed to enjoy Jenni's performance greatly (as did I) and his female counterpart let tiny gaps appear in the armour of her inscrutability. Fennel seemed to physically shrink under the welter of questions she faced and yet the judge repeatedly stopped Jenni just at the point when the thrust of her argument was reaching its target.

When we took a break, she confided in me.

'In any other case I've done you'd be punching the air now because you'd know you'd won. But I can't seem to crack this judge. I'm scoring points at will and yet he is putting me down', she said, and I agreed. Jenni had reduced her opponent to a speechless shell and given her every opportunity to flounder. Fennel seemed to seize each of these opportunities and relish her own fragility. Removed from the safety of her cabal she simply wasn't up to the job of justifying her actions. With genuine opposition she came across as a flawed person with flawed logic.

I was dismayed by Judge Russell's attitude, but these were early days.

Chapter Six

Mr Wenman, Nurse

Next up was Wenman, a nurse, and he didn't disappoint. I had already given Jenni my honest appraisal of him and he displayed every trait I'd given him, like an actor getting into character. I'd said that he was pompous and arrogant and he was. He was a gift to us because he portrayed himself so unsympathetically that it would be a major difficulty for anyone to give credence to his testimony, even if it sounded reasonable, which it did not. I was quite sure that the judges simply wouldn't like him. The following extract is of Jenni's prepared questions. She knew the answers but wanted to hear him admit the truth or lie.

Mr Wenman

For how long did you deliberate?

You had to examine the reasoning of the first panel to see if it was appropriate – with reference to the evidence produced to them. (252) What were the reasons of the first panel for dismissing?

There's no letter explaining their reasons, so you had the minutes at 213 (a) and what Mr Neath told you as a witness in the appeal. That's all isn't it?

Mr Neath could not provide your panel with any reasons - so you didn't have any reasons to examine. How could you fulfil your task as an appeal panel if you could not examine why the first panel had dismissed?

So everything your panel did was based on the presumption of why the first panel had dismissed?

Either that or you were not concerned with why they had dismissed?

Policies and procedures adopted by the body are contractual?

Which ones did you think ought to have been in use?

Did you have them in front of you at the hearing?

Why not?

Did you consider that Mr Roy was 'underperforming'? Had become de-skilled?

*Go to 370 at * didn't Mr Roy fit this bill?*

See page 272 at * What safeguarding issues?

Did you examine <u>the documents</u> to ascertain the facts before turning this appeal ground down in such a peremptory manner?

Did Ms Barrish take you through any document which said previously dismissed cases could be raked up again for sanction?

See 281 and 284 you say in your statement that these are your reasons for upholding the dismissal, yes?

Your job was to consider the grounds of appeal. Page 32 Where are your responses to those grounds?

Sensitive to stressors - duty to remove? Look at page 371 at * and then 378. You don't have a duty to 'remove' as you put it, until the teacher has had a chance to be helped, do you?

Neither Ms Fennel, nor the disciplinary panel, nor your panel offered a chance for Mr Roy to be helped, did they?

What effect did Ms Maddox's information have on your panel?

Did it make you consider how the evidence from other people used by Ms Fennel had been obtained?

Why then did you allow or take any notice of Mrs Casson's evidence. What was the effect of Mrs Casson's evidence? I see you referred to her in your reasons.

Or Mrs Summerlee's?

Did you read what the disc procedure says about appeals?

This was not a rehearing = quote 252

Pygmalion: Did you read it? Did you appreciate its significance? 462, 474

Were you told that the failure to deal adequately with pupil behaviour was having a significant impact on morale and energy?

Did you have that in mind when you set down in your reasoning at numbers 3,4,5, and 6? on 281

Look at number 6 - He should have read Policy 25 ? Go to the previous page. Mr Fisher is talking about the bullet points on the back of the original decision (213 (a) Why should Mr Roy be castigated for not reading the document?

Had you read it? How do you know how relevant it was?

Go to 338. Had you read this? Note the date. You knew of this policy and its contents when you confirmed the dismissal in October. What does 'important policy in terms of staff protection' mean?

Staff would be protected from dismissal if they had acted within the policy?

See 360. Did this have no effect on your thinking at all?

In your panel's reasons for confirming the dismissal on page281 "action did not justify the restraint used" - whose action?

This is allegation 3 – JS ? Mr Roy is standing in front of a door. He was standing there while a 16 year old boy ran into another room to try and escape detention, - i.e. well before this youth rushed at him and decided to push him out of the way to get through the door behind him. Behind that half open door was a crowd of shouting youngsters egging him on crammed into a narrow corridor. Are you seriously telling me that Mr Roy had no right (as per this procedure) to 'stand in the way of a student who may endanger others if allowed to pass' and had no reason to see this as "a person behaving in a way which compromises good order"?

Jenni asked him to explain why he had upheld the decision of the disciplinary hearing but he couldn't remember in any detail what I had been accused of, let alone justify his actions. He couldn't explain why he thought I was guilty. He didn't know what legislation he had used to reach his decision. He accepted that there was a safeguarding issue, without knowing what was normally required for the appropriate legislation to be invoked. Jenni repeatedly gave him opportunities to explain himself and he repeatedly failed to do so.

When pushed he became very brusque and was often quite rude. Unlike Fennel he never quite lost the power of speech even if what he said would have been better left unsaid. When challenged about looking at his watch and being concerned about the length of time he was being kept he denied that this was so. This was a plain lie, not stupidity or incompetence, although to the uninitiated it might have been difficult to separate simple deceit from the mix containing the other two.

When questioned about his wording at one point he made mention of the fact that these were the sorts of words he would use at work and that he was a nurse. He never failed to get a mention of his new medical career in. He also mentioned his voluntary career as a commissioned officer in St John Ambulance at which point Jenni cast a glance in my direction. I just shook my head. As I explained to her later, becoming a commissioned officer in that particular organisation was not a particularly onerous undertaking. It was not to be taken as a guarantee of quality or moral fibre as say, a year at Sandhurst, Dartmouth or Cranwell might be. Some of the 'commissioned officers' I had met in my short time with St John Ambulance were not drawn from the upper echelons of society. They were not a uniformly splendid bunch.

He was every bit as rattled as his predecessor in the stand had been but rather than withdrawing into a protective cocoon of reticence he became forceful and loud. It was a shocking performance. The barrister representing the school must have wilted inwardly as he blustered and pontificated. It was clear that he had just gone along with whatever direction Fennel (or should that be Captain Janeway?) had given him. He clutched at every thorn of idiocy thrown in his direction. His reputation would deteriorate still further in the months ahead but for the meantime he'd done us a great service. If the judges had any doubt about the calibre and outlook of the people I had been up against then those doubts were surely extinguished.

Again, Judge Russell had seemed almost obstructive towards Jenni and yet there could be no doubt that she had carried the day. His two colleagues seemed to have got the measure of their man and the male panellist had again thoroughly enjoyed the theatre of Jenni's cross-examination. There was simply no hiding place for the witnesses and I have to confess I revelled in their discomfiture. For the first time someone was putting my case across strongly and someone was listening to that case with an open mind. Almost everything that Jenni said further eroded the credibility of the school. It would have been impossible to deduce from the proceedings that I had been given a fair trial. The discrepancies, deceit, disarray... the conflict, confusion, contradiction... it was all on an epic scale. The enormity of the injustice was obvious on the very first day. I could only hope that Judge Russell's reserve could be explained away by the fact that he was playing devil's advocate.

On day two Jenni started on the HR people whose main crime was that of bungling. Apart from Carol Gee, who I came to view as Fennel's confidante and ally, there were two others involved: Richard Darby and Lynn Barrish. Darby had been there to assist Neath and Barrish to assist Wenman. In addition, Darby had effectively deputised for Neath when the latter was unable to attend the appeal, through an injured back.

Gee was a stern, unsympathetic character, very much a functionary but apparently without a functionary's grasp of the rules. There had been times when it had seemed to get rather personal for her and I detected a certain amount of animosity. There was no doubt that she was there to assist in the process of removing me from my post rather than ensuring that a fair procedure was followed, with the reasonable aim of establishing the truth. She had accompanied Fennel on their trip to see Doctor Watson from Occupational Health when he had completely missed the point of our meeting, that being to establish that I was a dangerous lunatic.

I can't help but reiterate the fact that his advice was sought as part of an investigation into my suitability for teaching but then disregarded simply because he saw no reason for me not to resume my job. That they had to go and see him to 'put him right', sounded like a form of bullying to me but the good doctor resolutely failed to discredit me. Gee became part of the disreputable clique rather than an objective advisor. On one occasion she had barely been able to conceal her ire when I told her that I would be unable to attend an appointment with Doctor Watson because I would be on holiday at Easter.

'So, you're not going to go to the meeting?', she fumed. A refusal to attend a meeting in term time would have aided her cause; I was obliged to go.

'I won't be here', I corrected, patiently. The appointment was rearranged and there was nothing that she could do about it.

I have included a selection of Jenni's questions for Gee. Many of these refer to points of law and the appropriate use of legislation, things which I could never have brought into the tribunal. Jenni's expertise far exceeded that of any of her opposite numbers. I had warned Jenni that Gee might be her most formidable opponent, but it was a relative term of course.

Have you been trained in the law as it affects schools' personnel?

Do you accept Collegiate is an LEA-maintained school with delegated budget?

Do you accept that, as a result, the governing body is the rightful respondent to this claim? and that they alone are responsible for determining whether a teacher should be dismissed by the LEA?

Do you accept that the regulation of discipline and capability of staff in the school and any procedures in relation to those is to be under the control of the governing body?

Do you accept that only the governing body can decide whether a teacher is suitable to work at their school or should be dismissed?

And that decision can only be made by way of two hearings at which the teacher has the opportunity to put his side of the case?

Do you accept that there was so much concern about the way allegations against teachers are handled nationally that last year there was a parliamentary select committee enquiry into the matter? It is on page 395 to 445. Look just for a moment at page 401. READ

Do you receive the circulars that the Department for Education sends out to all schools and Local Authorities setting out advice on such matters?

Do you accept that schools are expected to consider that advice?

So you know that teachers are entitled to a careful and objective process in the handling of any allegations made against them?

And an objective investigation?

See page 77 There had been a strategy meeting the day before which you attended. This meeting decided no Police or Social Services processes would be pursued and the matter would be handled internally - yes?

After that strategy meeting on 7th January there were two more (18th March at 319 and 11th June at 343...) but only you, Ms Fennel and Kate Ryding attended those two, yes?

The minutes of the second one - at 321 shows a decision was made at the first one that Mr Roy was currently unsuitable to work with children.

Turn to page 307 - the minutes of a strategy meeting you attended. See page 308 READ

You accept, do you, that every piece of information imputed into this meeting came orally from you or the head? That there were no medical reports or papers of any sort shared at the meeting? and that Mr Roy was not present to fight his corner?

How do you explain "John who had experienced bullying from Mr Roy and who had also been grabbed by the throat." It is untrue, isn't it?

243

Did you think that this strategy meeting was a strategy meeting under ACPC guidance to consider a strategy of how best to protect a child who had been harmed, or a meeting to consider a strategy to deal with Mr Roy?

Did you find the process in these meetings balanced and objective?

Do you accept that neither Ms Ryding nor any strategy meeting has a right to decide a teacher is unfit for work?

Do you know that such a decision is subject to specific statute and can only be determined after a hearing of medical evidence? (See 378) updated in 2003 to the Education (Health Standards) (England) Regulations 2003.

These meetings vastly exceeded their powers and stage managed the way Mr Roy's case was progressed without adequate investigation, didn't they?

I was asked by your solicitor, Mr Mottershead, what the Pygmalion report was, when asking for disclosure, because neither you nor he knew what it was. Was the HR department unaware of this process?

You knew, surely, that there was mounting concern about lack of support for staff in disciplinary situations at the school?

You knew that Mr Roy was saying that it was the context for his lack of capability in the classroom?

You had his Personnel File. See page 304 re Debbie in September 2008 - what was that telling you ?

And then on 31ˢᵗ March 2009, six months later (page 327 READ)

This was a serious and unfair situation teachers were in at this school, Miss Gee, See 465 and 474 wasn't it?

It was arguably negligent to let it continue, wasn't it?

See what the government says a teacher can expect - 164 and 165

But when Mr Roy articulated this you decided he was 'unbalanced' [ref if nec to286] or had a medical problem?

Go to313 – sent home because he was not coping under the Council's duty of care?

The OHP doctor didn't say that an illness caused him to assault children, despite your visit to sort him out, so you had to get rid of Mr Roy another way, didn't you?

So you moved to discipline? You agreed to do this in the second strategy meeting at 321. Were you responsible for the writing of the letter at 323?

Page 286 / 287 is your preparation of Ms Fennel for the appeal. ? Read it all. Why were you so desperate to get Mr Roy dismissed?

Para 6 of your statement - where did you get the last two lines from? They are not on 536.

Para 7 - you refer to another document and quote from it in this paragraph. At the end of your recitation of part of it you say "the governors reviewed this as part of their deliberation of the evidence provided to them." It's not true, is it? The governors did not have this document in front of them - not one of the appendices (I disclosed it for this tribunal)

How do you know, anyway, what the governors did when they deliberated? You weren't there.

How do you know (para 8 on page 6) that the governors' final decision was "unanimous following careful consideration of all the facts"? You weren't there.

You comment on some documents in the bundle in paragraph 10. Do you understand what you have written?

I don't propose to plough through it all but I must deal with the serious misconception: You say in the middle of page 7 that an important document has been superseded . You place a lot of reliance on the generic document April 2006 <u>DCSF Working Together to Safeguard Children</u> :a guide to inter-agency working to safeguard and promote the welfare of children : a massive document (200 plus pages) to provide a framework to prevent children slipping through the net between agencies after the Victoria Climbie enquiry. (There's just one section in the bundle at 534)- yes?

But the Education Sector has its own specific requirements beyond this generic one, doesn't it?

The document at 480 - which you say has been superseded is still part of the guidance a school SHOULD use, isn't it?

There was much flicking through the two voluminous bundles and peering and thumbing but suffice to say that whilst the investigation had been sufficiently thorough to pass inspection by a group of lay people who believed everything they were told and who were unlikely to go against the advice of the headteacher in any case, it was not up to scratch in any other sense. It was botched and had I not taken them to this tribunal and not had Jenni examining every detail, turning every rotten stone, no-one would ever have known how these people conducted their business.

Chapter Seven

Neath Goes Under

On day three it was the turn of Neath, the governor who had led the disciplinary panel towards their guilty verdict. I had told Jenni that in my view he was dodderer and that he could be unzipped like a banana. I might as well have written a script for him, so unerringly helpful was he.

Again, he couldn't explain why I had been dismissed other than some vague recollection that it had seemed to be the right decision based on the evidence he had been presented. Pressed for some detail it was clear that he had only a sketchy recollection of what I had purportedly done. He couldn't explain what gross misconduct was, even though I was dismissed for it. He admitted that the first charge against me had been used as evidence during my hearing, something that my opponents had tried to deny. He made himself appear utterly clueless, rather than malicious, although it was clear that he cared not for my fate. It was very satisfying to see him crumble. It was pitiable but only what I felt he deserved.

I have included a selection of the battery of questions directed at the hapless Neath.

Tell me why the panel decided Mr Roy should be dismissed that very day and should not be given a period of notice.

Tell me about this part of your deliberations. What did the other members of the panel say about giving notice?

For how long did you deliberate after the hearing?

Do you accept that your task as a panel in that time was to (A) make findings about what actions Mr Roy had actually done, (B) then to decide if any of them were wrong - and then (C) decide what sort of sanction, if any, they merited?

OK - Tell me what you found Mr Roy actually DID in incident 1?

What did you find that he DID in incident 2?

Do you accept that there was a shortage of primary evidence on incident 2?

Was it not of concern to the panel?

What did you find that he DID in incident 3?

What was his error in in incident 1?: behaviour so gross that Mr Roy's family had to be deprived of its income that very day ?

How could you find him guilty of gross misconduct for this when due process had exonerated him?

Incident 2 – On what evidence did you decide that Mr Roy <u>had</u> grabbed the boy? Why?

You had x –v- y to weigh. They were contradictory. To help you decide between them you had circumstantial evidence (the boy had told his mother and Mrs Summerlee more or less the same story, and on Mr Roy's behalf no-one in a hall full of potential witnesses had seen the incident take place.) What did you rely on to decide Mr Roy was lying?

You knew the boy, his mother, and the investigating senior teacher were totally satisfied with the outcome at the time. There was no disciplinary process brought by Mrs Summerlee, and Mr Roy continued to work at the school. You knew these things, didn't you?

What did you find that made this such gross misconduct that he now had to be instantly dismissed?

Mr Neath, your panel simply did not have enough weight on the scales to allow it to say Mr Roy probably assaulted the lad, did it? What was the evidence then?

You say in para 5 of your statement that without incident one, you would still have made the same decision on incident two and three.

In respect of these two incidents: did Mr Roy have the opportunity to challenge Jake about his story (the chance to say "which wall did I push you against? Which pupils asked you if you were OK? You have exaggerated this haven't you?) NO - Ms Fennel did not challenge him either, did she?

He did not come as a witness to the panels, so extra care should have been applied to make sure his evidence was tested - particularly when Mr Roy said he had not grabbed the boy. It wasn't, was it?

Did Mr Roy have any opportunity to challenge John about his behaviour in the classroom? Or ask him about shoving him out of the way? Ms Fennel did not question him and say "Tell me how you came to be pushing your teacher out of the way, or how did you move Mr Roy from the door?" Did she?

The issue of the boy's behaviour was completely unexplored, wasn't it? Didn't it matter what he was doing?

Didn't it matter when you were assessing whether Mr Roy had a right to apprehend him, what he was doing and what he had done?

If he'd been shouting "get out of my way you fucking bastard" would that have made any difference to Mr Roy's right to apprehend him?

The point is - nobody asked him, and Mr Roy was suspended and not allowed to ask him.

We have looked at incident 2. Let's examine incident 3

Allegation 3 - You had evidence from Mr Roy and Mr Dodd, in person, and nothing from JS to deny it, that JS had aggressively and physically forced his teacher away from a door to get through it. You had evidence from Ms Maddox and Ms England that seconds later Mr Roy was holding the boy by his coat lapels. Do you believe it is wrong to hold a miscreant who has just assaulted you by his coat lapels?

Is it so wrong that a teacher has to be instantly dismissed?

Did you have any advice or documents that told you that holding him by his coat lapels was gross misconduct? No - you had to apply judgment. Could you apply judgment without knowing what behaviour Mr Roy was reacting to?

You had no evidence of Mr Roy losing his temper, did you?

No evidence of his exerting more force than was necessary to prevent the boy running off,

No evidence of his hitting the boy in any way?

No evidence of his holding him in a way that might hurt him, did you?

You had evidence from all four teachers that this incident was in the context of the boy's refusal to follow a legitimate instruction, violence from the boy, and a gang of pupils egging him on in a narrow corridor. Do you have any reason to say that he was NOT engaging in behaviour prejudicial to maintaining good order and discipline?

Tell me on what basis you hold that a teacher cannot physically intervene with a pupil to maintain good order and discipline?

Did you consider what the results might have been of him running full-tilt into a constricted space crammed with other pupils?

Look at 484 and READ and go to 490. Did you have this circular in front of you?

Was it brought to your attention?

Did you consider what you are required to consider at the bottom of page 490?

The allegation you found proved? [Read it from Report on page 37] Why do you consider that "any form of physical intervention" is gross misconduct"?

Darby - page 207 - what safeguarding measures?

What legislation are you talking about here as chairman?

Did anybody show this legislation?

Did Mr Darby take you to any document, or show you any quotation when he gave you this advice?

Pygmalion: as a governor you would know that there was a major impediment to the school moving forward - yes? Teachers have a right to 165/164, don't they?

Pygmalion was saying these provisions weren't in place - big time - 474 and 462. Wasn't this important for considering Mr Roy's evidence?

If the school negligently was putting teachers in an unacceptable position, and not supporting them, doesn't that impact on their health or behaviour?

Shouldn't you have considered this idea?

At this time the LEA removed the head from the school because it was going downhill, didn't they?

Suddenly and without giving the statutory notice? Leaving you with a vacancy and a caretaker head?

Let's examine 213 (a) You say the panel THEREFORE uphold the headteacher's submission that Mr Roy be dismissed forthwith

Your headteacher made the decision and you went along with it, didn't you?

Your job on the governing body is to support the head's running of the school, isn't it, and that's what happened here.

You just accepted the head's recommendation and her reasoning?

The only reasoning you gave the appeal panel was hers - he might reoffend. Where's your reasoning?

The panel THEREFORE uphold means that what is before that in the text constitutes your reasons for coming to that decision - yes? Why do you wriggle? What were your reasons if not the ones that were written down? Has someone told you since that they are inadequate?

Let's look at them: The first two depend on the causing of distress. Why is the causing of distress gross misconduct?

Why is not being able to prove you have sought guidance gross misconduct?

Why is not reading and understanding a document gross misconduct? Did you check the applicability of this document?

You couldn't be sure he would not reoffend - why does that mean what he did constitutes gross misconduct?

You had been told (page 277) by Mrs Summerlee that such an incident was out of character for Mr Roy who upheld the school rules, hadn't you?

You attended the appeal hearing to tell the first panel what your reasoning had been, didn't you? See what Mr Fisher says - third bullet point up on page280.

Let's look at what you told the appeal panel (279) (read the section).

Why was Mr Darby present?

Look at *. The head suggested a penalty and you agreed with it?

The only reason you give the hearing for Mr Roy's gross misconduct dismissal, as far as I can see is: "on the balance of probabilities this could happen again." What would happen again?

Do you accept that the first incident was an accident and that Mr Roy did not lose his temper during that dreadful lesson?

Do you accept that Mrs Summerlee (deputy head) saw no reason to report any misconduct to the head after investigating and dealing with the second incident?

Do you accept that Mr Roy did not hit or lose his temper with John who had assaulted him in the third incident?

What fused these incidents together as evidence of the same feature?

What is the unifying feature? What did you have three examples of that was likely to happen again?

Tell me, Mr Neath, what the difference is between misconduct and gross misconduct?

Tell me what you have to do in order to establish something on the balance of probabilities?

Possibility isn't probability is it?

Have you had any training as a governor in your duties if put on a disciplinary panel?

Without adequate reasoning you could have had no genuine belief in Mr Roy's guilt, could you?

Wasn't part of your investigation to see if the correct procedure had been used?

Did you consider the head had dealt with Mr Roy's 'inappropriate behaviour' under the right procedure - given that he told her he was struggling?

Shouldn't you have decided that the matter should be dealt with under the capability procedure?

Look at the capability procedure (page 370 to start with) at * then **

Go to 369 and 371. This is the process that should have been incepted for someone saying they couldn't cope, isn't it?

You had to examine the reasoning of the first panel to see if it was appropriate – with reference to the evidence produced to them.

It would be logical for me to have included Neath's responses to the above questions but there are four reasons why I have not done so. Firstly, his answers were repetitive, nonsensical, vague and increasingly monosyllabic. Secondly, I can't actually remember them in detail. Thirdly, the questions above are quoted verbatim from Jenni's script but many more were added and some dispensed with as the cross examination got under way. Fourthly, Jenni formulated each of her questions in the secure knowledge that Neath could make no reasonable defence. The only respite from the inquisitive barrage was that afforded by the need to locate pages and paragraphs in the appropriate documentation (hence the page numbers). It was obvious that he was seeing these for the first time. It is an understatement to say that he floundered but if he thought that was the end of it he was soon to be disabused.

When Jenni had finished it was Judge Russell's turn to question him. The change in his attitude was remarkable, as if someone had flicked a switch labelled 'go for the kill'. I was stunned. His diffidence had gone and in its place was his obvious and profound disbelief at the process which had led to my downfall. It was a disbelief that he didn't try to disguise; indeed, it was etched on his face the way that some of us might have laughter lines or duelling scars.

He was very clinical as he went about it but gave Neath ample opportunity to dig himself out of the hole he was in. Neath only increased the depth of the hole with his artless attempts at explanation, setting new standards for ineptitude in the process.

'So, you are saying that the first offence was considered when making your decision to dismiss Mr Roy?'

'Yes sir.'

'So even though he had been exonerated of any blame you decided that you could investigate the matter for a second time?'

'Yes sir.'

The judge's brow furrowed noisily.

'If you were to consider Mr Roy's first alleged offence in isolation what punishment would you deem to be appropriate?'

'Well we didn't consider it in isolation it was part of a pattern of events....'

'Yes, but that isn't what I asked you. I asked you to consider the first offence by itself. So, if you found Mr Roy guilty in that instance and no other, what would you deem to be the appropriate punishment?' There was a hint of patient exasperation in the Judge's voice. Not contempt but he certainly acted as if he was in the presence of a dim child. Neath was floored by the question and unsure how to answer.

'Well I suppose a written warning, maybe.'

'A written warning?'

'Yes.'

'Even though when the matter was investigated Mr Roy was exonerated of any blame?', asked the Judge. All eyes were on Neath.

'Well it was part of a pattern and there were safeguarding issues to consider….'

'But if Mr Roy was found to be innocent then how could that be part of a pattern in which you claim two children were hurt by Mr Roy?'

'Well a girl was hurt in the first incident.'

'So, was that accidental or on purpose?'

'Oh, I think it was an accident', Neath assured us all.

'So, for this accident you believe that Mr Roy should have received a written warning?' Neath made no coherent reply. He looked like a man staring defeat in the eyes but the Judge wasn't finished with him.

'So, for the second incident Mr Neath, taken in isolation, what punishment would you deem to be appropriate if Mr Roy was found guilty?'

'Well, we thought that the second incident was part of a pattern....'

'Yes, but I want you to tell me what you would have given Mr Roy as a punishment if you had found him guilty of that incident and no other.'

'Well, I suppose a verbal warning, maybe', replied Neath meekly. There was no conviction to anything that he said from this point on.

'A verbal warning?'

'Yes, a verbal warning', confirmed Neath. By now he clearly wondered what the hell was happening to him. Where were all the nice people who simply agreed with what he said? Why couldn't it be that nice Ms Fennel sitting there instead of these nasty people? All three Judges scribbled furiously as Neath unravelled like an Egyptian Mummy getting ready for bed. He was plumbing new depths of verbal disharmony but his uncontrolled descent wasn't over yet and there would be no coming up for air either. At some point Jenni leaned over and scribbled on my pad, 'You've just won your tribunal!' I felt like crying. I was engulfed in a small tidal wave of emotion but had to carry on as if nothing had happened. Churchill might have described it as the beginning of the end and I certainly recognised it as such. The war wasn't won but the decisive battle had been.

The judge's assault continued.

'So, if you were looking at the third incident in isolation what punishment would you give Mr Roy?', he asked. By now Neath had learned to dispense with the 'it was considered as part of a pattern' argument.

'Well, maybe a verbal warning again.'

There was a hiatus as the Judges scribbled. Jenni looked at me and smiled.

'So, what you are saying is that if three lesser punishments are aggregated they equal a dismissal?'

'Well it was the accumulation of Mr Roy's behaviour we thought that....'

'So, a written warning and two verbal warnings equals a dismissal?', persisted the judge. Neath seemed to concur with this view.

'What exactly did Mr Roy do that constituted Gross Misconduct?'

'Well, he had harmed three children.'

'Had he?'

'Yes, in all three cases children were harmed', stated Neath, erroneously.

'The first case you agreed was an accident. And in the other two incidents there is no record of any harm coming to any of the children.' His point made, he carried on.

'Did you believe that the boy in the second incident was telling the truth?'

'Yes.'

'Why was that?'

'Because he said so and when he was asked again he said so again.'

'So, Mr Roy is a liar?'

'Well, I wouldn't say that….'

'But you just have. If the boy says that Mr Roy pinned him against the wall and Mr Roy says that he didn't and you believe the boy then Mr Roy must be a liar.'

It got to the point that the judge didn't wait very long for Mr Neath's answers simply because he knew that none were forthcoming. Further questioning revealed that Neath barely understood the role of a governor in these situations. His understanding of the appropriate legislation was less than sketchy. He relied entirely on ideas that he didn't understand and relied too much on the advice of HR. It would soon be their turn and they would fare no better.

At some point we had been joined by visitors, both of whom sat behind me and whispered enthusiastically. We all assumed that they were from the press but we later discovered through chatting to them in the claimant's waiting room that they were just interested bystanders. One of them was a sacked teacher and the other some sort of representative but I never quite got to bottom of their sudden appearance at my tribunal. The younger of the two, a voluble Asian man – the sacked teacher – was extremely agitated on my behalf having heard part of the case against me. I wasn't sure whether or not to even discuss it with him and Jenni was polite but guarded. The other man was a lugubrious character, more restrained than his companion and yet equally sure that he had seen enough to know that an injustice had occurred. We never saw them again, but I couldn't help but think that they were engaged in some sort of espionage – such was my paranoia!

From that moment on my future looked rather brighter. Simply to hear someone putting across the arguments that I had been making for months was gratifying enough but to find that they now had a receptive audience was truly refreshing. These people were exposed for what they were at last and it was as if they were in the dock in my place. It must have been a big shock for them. They were in the business of keeping everything watertight but instead they had produced the leakiest boat possible to float their case on.

By the end of day three it became clear that it would be impossible to hear testimony from my witnesses in the allotted time and so they were stood down and the final day set aside to deal with the remainder of the school's witnesses, namely Barrish. It must have been deeply unsettling for her to appear last having seen the fate of her predecessors on the stand. Blackpool Borough Council's credibility had gone entirely and with it that of Fennel, its former employee. There was no escape for the hapless Barrish, no reasonable defence that she could offer and no throwing in of the towel. They couldn't even reshape their arguments to suit their new circumstances. The damage was irrevocable.

Chapter Eight

Interlude

I returned to work the following day, hopeful that my life could eventually return to normal. We were sent off to cover British Superbikes at Donnington, me fervently hoping that no-one would be so rash as to fall from their motorcycle and require any medical attention. The thought of trying to reattach a severed leg using the scant knowledge at my disposal filled me with terror. In truth I had other things on my mind, replaying the events of the last few days, re-examining the evidence, thinking about my future.

The repetitive buzz of two-wheeled projectiles did nothing to divert me. If you have never seen motorbike racing and aren't interested in it then avoid; it's dull beyond belief. My companion on that little trip was a bike fan and a keen conversationalist. We had little in common and when, at one point, I attempted to read my book he accused me of being a 'lone shark'. Not a loan shark. I presume he meant to say that I was a lone wolf.

Luckily no one parted company with their bike in such a way as to require much in the way of medical attention and our day was packed with inaction.

I had plenty of time to consider the events of the past few days and to sum up my new position. My enemies were in disarray and had suffered a major reverse; the question was, would the next four months give them time to regroup, for we were scheduled to resume hostilities in August? This apparently suited Fennel, who had no job, and the HR bods who worked during the summer anyway, but was less than convenient for my witnesses for whom the timing meant taking time off from their summer break. A cynical man might think it was just another underhand but deniable trick from the school.

Their case – that I was rightly dismissed and remained so – seemed to have suffered a mortal blow. When one considered the damage that they had inflicted upon themselves it was hard to imagine the situation improving for them once my witnesses were 'unleashed'. Fennel had come unstuck and made it seem as if her grasp of reality was weak. She had become Humphrey Bogart's character Captain Queeg in the Caine Mutiny. If you have seen that film you will understand what I mean, if not then disregard that sentence. The HR people had proven themselves to be incompetent and ready to go to any lengths to maintain the viability of their case, even in so far that they were prepared to alter the wording of the documents upon which they relied. Jenni had exposed their deceit in this respect on at least one occasion. The judges could only look on in disbelief. Neither Wenman nor Neath could explain why I had been dismissed. Their grasp of the proper way to conduct investigations or hearings was negligible.

In short it all seemed unfair and amateurish. The judges must have begun to suspect their motives and no doubt they had seen cases of staff being pushed out simply for exposing awkward truths. They now knew what sort of school I had been working at and must have sympathised with me and the predicament I had found myself in. These were people who had attended school in the days when discipline was maintained and expected by all concerned. Without doubt they found the story of my downfall disturbing. How could they not be appalled?

Those who had conducted the case against me were an unsympathetic bunch but even had they not been, there was no ignoring the facts... not anymore.

We returned to our usual work routine in May, two ambulances signing on with control each day and taking the sick to hospital. I wondered if this was my future. I enjoyed meeting the patients, taking their blood pressure, pulse et cetera and chatting to them about the exact reason for their imminent trip to hospital. I grew in confidence and within the limits of my training found that I wasn't too bad at the job. I enjoyed the driving also, finding a peculiar tranquillity behind the wheel, especially when my crew mate was in the back with a patient. I think I would have enjoyed it more had it not been for the requirement to have two crew members – maybe I *was* a lone shark as had been suggested! My methods were often at odds with those of my crewmates which made for simmering discord and eventual resentment.

Soon we in Transport Services found ourselves in a virtual civil war. The volunteers had never managed to get over their distrust of the Transport Services staff. We had come in and taken their ambulances and threatened to destroy the goodwill they had established over a number of years… It was all rubbish and I never really understood the logic of their argument. In April the key had been stolen from the coded cabinet on the exterior wall of the garage meaning that none of us could get in until the caretaker was summoned. Later the combination on the key cabinet for the medical gases was changed so that we couldn't exchange our oxygen or Entonox at the start of a shift. It remained locked for months until someone smashed it open and took the key, at which point we were no further on.

The St John website was inundated with libellous comment on our activities and one anonymous volunteer comically, tried to start a strike with a banner headline, 'Strike Lancashire!'. Very dramatic. How they could strike and exactly who would care was beyond us all; it came to nothing. The situation was farcical and not helped by the fact that *some* (and only some) of their criticisms might have been justified. With regard to our operational preparedness there were questions which could legitimately have been asked. Often, we were short of stock, simply because the large-waisted man in charge of replenishing our medical supplies rarely made it available to us. Sometimes it was there but locked away. No matter how much we complained about the situation it never changed.

Eventually a few of the dissident volunteers were rooted out and executed. Or dishonourably discharged. Or whatever you do with volunteers. They served as an example to the others and an uneasy truce was unofficially established. I found it all ridiculous; not faintly so. The revelation that Wenman was a commissioned officer in St John Ambulance added to my reservations; it was appalling to think that a man of that calibre might actually outrank me in some sense. On one occasion I met with a volunteer from Blackpool. By way of casual conversation, I asked her if she was a volunteer and she haughtily replied that she was a commissioner. Perhaps she expected me to stand to attention or salute, in which case she is still waiting. I stood corrected but attempted to make conversation with her nevertheless (we were under instruction to do so, now). I asked her what she did for a living and she replied that she worked in a Blackpool school. At this point I told her a little about myself and my recent past, all of which induced a blank look and nothing more. At once I realised that she already knew all about me and there was only one source for such information. Wenman's indiscretions would be his downfall.

As Diane's treatment got underway, life became more difficult for us. My shifts either started at 10.00 and finished at 20.00, or at 12.00 finishing at 22.00. This meant that when Diane was laid low I was able to drop the children off at school or at the childminder, but that Diane somehow had to collect them at the end of their day. Not only that but she had to make the tea, walk the dog, make packed lunches and then bath the children. It was too much, increasingly so. I began looking for other work, preferably with office hours. In all honesty there was also a touch of disillusionment setting in. It was clear that the Ambulance Service for whom we worked only really wanted us for discharges, urgents and so on but many of my colleagues still craved the more exciting stuff involving blue lights and defibrillators. As time went on I felt increasingly distant from my training in such things... but at least I realised it. I was also concerned that some of my more enthusiastic colleagues were also incapable of calm rational thought, prone to panic and making bad decisions. I didn't want to be around them. The small group of people whose judgement I trusted seemed rarely to be rostered with me.

Chapter Nine

Seconds out, Round Two

We took a family holiday in August, staying in Jenni's comfortable house in the beautiful French town of Montreuil. Our original plan had been to camp as we normally did but the offer of the house proved too much to resist, bearing in mind the debilitating effects of Diane's treatment. Much better to wallow in abject misery in a bed than on an inflated mattress inches above the French soil. We walked around the ramparts of the town, had picnics, trips to the beach and it was all very pleasant... apart from one thing: the imminent resumption of my tribunal. In April I had felt that victory was nearly within my grasp, as did Jenni. The enforced break suited neither of us but was unavoidable. My optimism hadn't disappeared in the meantime; far from it, I didn't see how my opponents could possibly turn things around but my complacency was gradually eroded as August drew near.

For one thing I would find myself in the witness box and although I was looking forward to finally giving my side of the story (the judges hadn't even heard me talk yet), I would have to be on my guard against being caught out by their barrister during cross-examination. In one sense I had nothing to worry about: I was innocent. I didn't have to lie about anything or remember which lies I had told or make sure that one lie didn't contradict another.

I didn't have to refer to any documentation or use it as justification for my actions; I had acted, not in accordance with a rule book through which I could leaf at my leisure, but instinctively, responding to situations that were forced upon me and which called for me to use my professional judgement. I had done so in good faith, in the reasonable expectation of support from the school authorities on whose behalf I worked. I think it was clear that I had done so but the fact remained that the barrister's job was to trip me up and force me to say something which didn't represent either my motivation or describe the actions precisely as they had occurred.

Descriptions of events could be twisted, malicious meanings attributed to innocent acts. This was, after all what I had had to put up with for a year and a half. If anyone was going to undo my hopes for reclaiming my innocence then it was me.

'It must have been very frustrating for you when children didn't do as you asked, Mr Roy.'

274

'Yes, it was indeed.'

'You must have felt like thumping someone', she said, jokingly.

'Not half!', he says jokingly and menacingly in equal measure.

As an interesting aside, almost the first person I bumped into, as I headed for Costa, was my old head of department. We chatted for a while and then parted company. As I made my way up the street, I recalled how, many years previously, I had taught a group of students and led them to some of the best results ever achieved in the school. Fifty-six per cent of them had gained a grade C or higher. The following year, this former head of science had taught their successors and the results had dropped to fourteen per cent. How had we fared in the intervening years? Well, obviously I had been sacked. He had left Collegiate many years previously and was now a science advisor working for some county council or other. My results had been exactly four times better than his, yet I got sacked whilst he got promoted. It makes you think, doesn't it? I'm not sure *what* it makes you think…. but it makes you think something.

There was no requirement for Fennel to attend this time. In fact, having given her testimony on that first day of tribunal in April, her presence had been superfluous (or, as that same head of science had once said in a moment of delicious redundancy, superfluous to requirements), except as a means of perpetuating the misery that she caused. I looked forward to her not being there because she gave me the creeps in the best of circumstances. I remember going to a friend's thirtieth birthday party and finding myself sitting next to Fennel for a time, engaged in desultory small talk. What an ordeal. To be fair she was no more enamoured with the situation than I was. Never was it clearer that we had nothing in common. Her tiny world was one to which I did not belong – and I was glad.

To my delight Fennel and her little friends quite unnecessarily deigned to turn up to the second half of the tribunal! There was no logical reason (other than masochism) for them to be there. Maybe they hoped that their presence would intimidate my witnesses into fluffing their lines. The spectacle, as far as they were concerned, was over and that had consisted of their case being rubbished, their integrity ruined and their short-sighted spite being made clear for all to see.

After the usual strained pleasantries, we got down to business and I was sworn in on a bible; despite having no religious affiliation I chose the conventional means of guaranteeing my honesty. This time only two judges were in attendance, the affable male panellist being absent following surgery. His absence had been agreed by both sides, although my opponents must have felt that they had most to gain when he had apparently been leaning in our favour.

I read my statement out and was then cross-examined by Jenni and the opposing barrister. Hers was only a token effort. There was no real conviction with anything she said as if she knew the battle and the war was lost. Presumably her orders were to carry on to save face or minimize the damage to the council's reputation. If that was her mission then it made Fennel's presence all the more mystifying for this was the council that had unceremoniously taken away her school. Did she hope to salvage her reputation? It was long gone, unsalvageable. Easier to raise the Titanic, in fact.

Sadly, I was my own worst witness, in part because I misunderstood the format of the cross-examination. The barrister made statements rather than asked questions and it made no sense for me to respond to them.

'It is true that you had admitted to Mrs Summerlee that you had pushed the boy against the wall', she said, rather than, 'did you admit to Mrs Summerlee....' To each of these statements I asked her if she wanted me to respond. It made the whole discourse rather stilted but fortunately she had very few angles of attack available to her, which meant that her cross-examination was rather perfunctory. There wasn't really any way in which she could trip me up or catch me out because all I had to do was tell the truth; I had woven no tangled web.

Tellingly, the judges had very few questions when it came their turn to speak. The female judge asked me to confirm that I had had no knowledge of my alleged admission of guilt in the second incident and that I had not been told what I was accused of prior to March 2009. Each of these assertions was perfectly true and so I could happily tell her so. Lucky for me; I am a terrible liar and in fact sometimes I feel and act as if I am lying when I am telling the truth. This usually only happens if I sense that person to whom I am speaking does not, or will not, believe me. I look guilty when I go through 'nothing to declare' at customs... and that's despite the fact that I genuinely have nothing to declare (except my mediocrity).

It would have been nice to know what the remaining two judges were thinking. I was fairly sure that their minds had been made up in April but had I now said something to make them change their minds? Not according to Jenni. Whilst it hadn't been an impressive performance it had been a transparently honest one and that was what really counted. My statement had been developed and refined over months. It said everything I wanted it to say – everything that I wanted to get off my chest, relevant or not! In particular I drew attention to the accusation of 'physical or indecent assault', something which I will neither forgive nor forget.

On the second and third days, Matthew Dodd, Sara Maddox and Allyson England gave their testimony. In addition, Martin Fisher returned to give his view on the procedures used to find me guilty. Despite my reservations about the union's role in my case it would be wrong to say that he was anything other than superb 'in the dock'. His statement was clear and unambiguous, his answers to cross-examination measured. He exuded calm and authority and was not even on one occasion lost for words. Asked if Wenman had repeatedly looked at his watch during my appeal (as I had claimed), he stated plainly that he wasn't sure if he had or not but that he was clearly pre-occupied with the time. This probably gave my assertion that he *had* repeatedly looked at his watch greater authority, simply because he didn't concur with the detail but rather with the principle. It is regrettable that the union and I subsequently fell out because Martin Fisher really showed his mettle.

Sara too was excellent and refused to be bowed by the cross-examination. She conceded not one point that the barrister made to undermine her. The contrast between her and the 'witnesses for the prosecution' could not have been greater; there is a lot to be said for honesty, integrity and intelligence, all of which she displayed in abundance. She had grown in stature and confidence as a witness and her determination to right a wrong was greater than ever. The gist of the barrister's efforts leaned towards intimating that she only changed her testimony because she was no longer at the school. It was the obvious tack to take and Sara refuted every word of it. Not only did it become clear that I had not assaulted the boy in question but that her evidence as it first appeared was terribly suspect.

Allyson, a shaky 'prosecution witness' at appeal, also kept calm and refused to be bullied. This is her statement, written and submitted when she still worked at the school:

Witness Statement of Allyson England

1.   My name is Allyson England. I work as Head of Year 7 at Collegiate High School. I make this statement knowing it will be put before an employment tribunal and believing all I say in it to be true.

2.   In December 2008 I was witness to the end of an incident between Mr Roy, a science teacher, and John *******, a year 10 boy, in the corridor. I came round a corner at the end of the school day with Ms Maddox to see Mr Roy, surrounded by a group of jeering pupils, firmly holding the coat of this boy to prevent him running off.

3.   This was in the context of major concern across the staff at that time about deteriorating pupil behaviour and the lack of support for teachers who tried to 'hold the line' and require good behaviour. I knew Mr Roy as a teacher respected by pupils and staff alike for his standards of both care and conduct.

4.   In view of the increasing level of aggression from the lad I asked Mr Roy to let him go – which he did. Ms Maddox took Jack into another room and I spoke briefly to Mr Roy. I had witnessed nothing from Mr Roy that indicated impropriety. His hold on the boy was not one likely to do him any hurt at all, and he had not lost his temper.

5.   On 17th December the head, Ms Fennel, interviewed me about the incident in the presence of Mrs Martin who was writing notes. What Mrs Martin wrote was produced as a 'statement' from me which I was asked to sign. It is on page 49.

6.   This first "statement" was taken the same day as Sara Maddox's. I was called into Ms Fennel's room, and she asked me what had happened. She did not tell me that her questioning was going to be used to create what she would later call a 'witness statement', or that it might be used at a hearing. She then told me not to discuss it with Sara. Later that morning, when I spoke to Polly Summerlee about the incident, Ms Fennel had me brought back to her

office and shouted at me for this, saying she had told me not to talk to anyone about it. I had to remind her that she had in fact said not to talk to Sara about this, rather than 'anyone'. The embargo on discussing the incident was different from how school incidents were normally handled.

7.   Because I was told not to talk about the statement with Sara it was not for a long time that the topic came up in conversation. At that point we agreed that we had both independently been amazed that Dave Roy had been sent home for this incident.

8.   We were actively discouraged from raising the topic of either this incident or the position of Mr Roy and I later found out that he had been forbidden under the terms of his suspension from contacting any staff, so for these two reasons I knew nothing of any subsequent events. However, months later in October 2009 I was required by Ms Fennel to be a witness for her in Mr Roy's appeal against dismissal. The staff had not been told that Mr Roy had been dismissed.

9.   I was called into the office to speak with Ms Fennel and Carol Gee. Ms Fennel informed me that I was going to be called as a witness for school against Mr Roy in his appeal hearing. I asked her if I had a choice as to whether to attend. She responded by implying that it was my professional duty to do so – and in the interests of safeguarding of pupils –

so I would have to attend. I remember her saying we all had to do things in our roles that we did not like to do. Carol Gee asked me some questions. They may well have been the ones on page 194. What I said was written down but I was never shown a copy of this second 'statement' It may well be that this 'statement' is the text at the bottom on page 194 (which I had never seen until the preparations for this tribunal) – except that I did not say at this time (or any other) that Dave Roy pushed John against the wall, or that he had John's coat by the shoulders because he did not do either of those things, so I do not know why Ms Fennel attributed them to me in this piece of text. I firmly said that he had him by the lapels, and that John was struggling to get his arms out of the coat, flailing his arms about.

10.   It was not until much later that I learned how the school's procedures provide for the taking of witness statements. This process was not applied to me. I was not offered the chance of being represented either time that a 'statement' was taken from me – including when I was spoken to by Ms Fennel and Carol Gee. The first time Mrs Martin recorded my 'statement'. The second time another person was in the room if I remember rightly, (Margaret Beaumont) who was working on the PC. At no point in either interview was I allowed to write my own account of events. Both times I was asked questions about features that Ms Fennel wanted to explore, rather than me setting down my

recollections of the chronology of the events and the context on the corridor. A document was produced which supposedly covered my answers. This was called a 'statement'.

11.   I was not given any written confirmation of the dates of the hearing, and was not given a copy of either of my 'statements' to look at in preparation for the hearing although I had seen the first briefly to sign it. However, after the appeal hearing was over, for some reason not explained to me I was given a copy of what I allegedly said by Mrs Martin. I had to make any amendments to this and send it back signed, but I said I would not sign it until it had been corrected because it was not what I remembered saying. To this day, I have never had an amended copy of the record of what I supposedly said.

12.   I found the appeal hearing very difficult. I felt that Ms Fennel and Mrs Gee wanted me to describe the incident in an incomplete and selective way. This was at variance with my memory of and reaction to the incident at the time, so I was over a barrel. At one point I was asked by the appeal panel if I was happy with the way my statement was taken. I answered yes, which was untrue. I was – to be honest - too nervous and too intimidated to answer as I should have done, i.e. that I was not happy with how information /statements had been both taken from me and used, and nor was I happy to have been

'primed' by Ms Fennel and Mrs Gee. That would have been very difficult to say in front of my headteacher.

13. I am recorded in the appeal hearing minutes only recently shown me (on page 276) as making comments in the appeal, but very few of the questions put to me are recorded, so my answers are out of context. The questions put to me seemed not to be 'open' questions. The answers were constrained and the questions asked in such a way as to not really provide any chance to qualify the resultant answer. There were no questions to elicit the effect on the situation of the other pupils involved, and none about whether I had seen any injury. I was not asked to explain whether in my view Mr Roy's manner of holding the boy was restraint or assault, and not asked about the amount of force used by Mr Roy.

14. I was asked if it was normal to grab a pupil in the way Mr Roy did, but not asked if it is normal for a pupil to assault a teacher to avoid going to detention. I was asked if I had reported it to anyone, and this was made to sound as though I had 'reported' Mr Roy's behaviour – which I hadn't. What actually happened was that Phil Chadwick had happened to be coming through the doors near room B13 when Dave Roy was going down the stairs. I explained John *******'s behaviour towards Dave Roy and told him to go after Dave to make

sure he was ok. When asked this same question by Carol Gee and Gill Fennel in their interview with me prior to the hearing, they had asked, "Did you feel that this was reporting it to someone who could deal with it?" I had said yes because Phil Chadwick was Second in Department and as such Dave Roy's line-manager. This was construed as me thinking Dave Roy's behaviour needed to be dealt with. This was not my view, and it was Phil Chadwick's role to follow up the behaviour of John ******* towards Dave Roy.

Allyson made it plain that she had felt coerced into making her previous testimony. She couldn't prove it but she didn't have to; the judges understood human nature and how 'things' were sometimes done. Fennel and co. had been desperate. As Jenni had pointed out previously they were seriously concerned lest my appeal was successful. It is interesting to wonder how they would have coped with a governor's decision that established I had been unfairly dismissed. How would they have integrated me back into my old job, especially when I had been written out of any timetable prepared for the new school year?

Allyson read her statement then was cross-examined. For me she was the final piece of the puzzle but for my opposite number hers was the final betrayal. Her testimony had much greater potency for the fact that she had apparently changed sides. The judges could only have suspected yet more subterfuge from the school; how else could any of this be explained? Again, she was only telling the truth. There was no fabricated story to get wrong.

Finally, Matthew Dodd was asked to give his version of events.

Witness Statement of Matthew Dodd

1. My name is Matthew Dodd. I am a teacher at the Respondent's school. I make this statement knowing it will be placed before an employment tribunal and believing all I say in it to be true.

2. I have been teaching since 2005 and when I came to the Collegiate High School I became aware of the professional behaviour of Mr Roy because we taught in the same Science Department. I tried to model myself on him because his practice was respected. He had such a well-disciplined classroom in such a difficult school, and was a model teacher – always willing to help and discuss the problems I encountered and suggesting ways of dealing with them, in particular poor behaviour.

3. During my time at the school and in the headship of Ms Fennel the exam results improved from a quite low base, but seemed to stall in 2007/2008. Pupil behaviour became a much bigger

problem and pupil numbers dropped. I personally felt pupil behaviour to be getting worse.

4. The Educational organisation Pygmalion was asked to examine the position to see what we could do to remedy the stall and move forward. All staff were given an anonymous questionnaire. 67 members of staff responded to it. A selection of staff were then interviewed. There was a staff meeting in which we were told that there were two key negative observations: the school had got 'stuck', and pupil behaviour was affecting staff morale and student motivation. This mirrored my own and my colleagues' views. Pygmalion said that in their research "there was a unanimous concern that the behaviour policy was confusing and did not work".

5. Mr Roy was a teacher who gave and expected high standards. I know- because he told me – that he found the deteriorating standards of pupil behaviour exceptionally difficult. His experience was that the actions of classroom teachers to maintain discipline were not 'backed up' by management. He felt, as did many others, that efforts to maintain it were betrayed.

6. On 16th December 2008 I was told by Mr Roy that he would come to my Year 10 lesson just before it ended to make sure a pupil, John *******, attended his detention – which was due to follow immediately afterwards. Mr Roy did so, and waited

at the back of the room, directly in front of the door, for the lesson to end. On seeing him John ******* bolted for the other exit at the other side of the classroom and out of the main classroom door to B12 but found it locked, I presume, and came back. John was shouting "I'm not doing a detention" to which Mr Roy calmly replied that he was, and that he should just sit down. I tried to explain to John that the sooner he sat down the sooner he could go home. I then moved across the classroom to let some pupils out of the door John had first bolted for. I was out of the classroom for a minute at the most but returned to see John pulling at the door and it banging into Mr Roy as he forced his way past him. Mr Roy followed John through the door and I lost sight of them for about twenty seconds. Then I saw Mr Roy holding John by the lapels outside the classroom with other teachers present.

7. When I went out of the room John ******* must have made straight for the door where Mr Roy was standing. I was aware of a group of pupils who had crowded outside the door in the narrow entrance corridor (slightly wider than a door's width and about 2 metres long). They were shouting and encouraging John. I did not see what happened to move Mr Roy from his position directly in front of the door, but did see John then pulling the door open into Mr Roy, hitting him with the door.

8. I crossed my room towards the incident. Mr Roy was calm but John was shouting, swearing. He was yelling "get off me" and was quite abusive (but I can't remember the actual dialogue) in trying to move away from Mr Roy. I was aware that two other teachers arrived on the scene and that Mr Roy let go of the coat.

9. On 17th December 2008 at 11.15 I was interviewed by the headteacher about this incident. Also present was Mrs Martin taking notes. The notes she took are at page 40 of the bundle. The interview took just under half an hour but the account written up by Mrs Martin is very short. It was brought to me during a lesson to sign so even though it was short I could not really give it my full attention. I was never told how it would be used. I was not asked to write my own account in my own words.

10. On 12th June 2009 I was called to the head's office and told that Mr Roy had told her that I had been in the assembly hall with him one morning break in December when there had been an incident with a year 7 pupil, by the name of Jim ******. She asked me to clarify it. She did not say for what purpose this was required. Again, I was not asked to write an account in my own words and I was not told what the allegation made by the boy was (or asked if I had witnessed such an event). Mrs Martin was present, writing notes, and again those notes (page 93) are much shorter than I would have expected

from the question and answer session I had taken part in. They thus appear to be a selective account of what I said.

11. I did remember being on duty with Mr Roy one day in December 2008 and hearing him shouting at a boy who apparently had misbehaved, and then watching him escort the boy out of the room, guiding him by his shoulders when necessary. Mr Roy then returned to the room to continue our break-time duty. I was later asked to sign the account typed up by Mrs Martin – again during a lesson. I did so, but wondered why Ms Fennel had not included all of the questions and answers. I was not told that this was either a witness statement or that it could be used in a disciplinary process.

12. I attended the disciplinary hearing to give my account of both incidents, after being contacted by Mr Fisher to do this (via a request made by him of the school). He was not allowed to contact me directly. I have been shown the minutes of this meeting on page 212 where my attendance is recorded, and I do not believe this fully sets out what I was asked or what I said on that occasion. In particular I take exception to how the interchange about the photograph was recorded. It gives the impression that I said Mr Roy was positioned near the wall. This was not the case and I did not suggest this. There was a queue of pupils and the welfare assistant (about 5 or 6 metres) between Mr Roy and

the nearest wall. I was simply indicating a slight variation in position from the one Mr Fisher showed me, by saying "nearer the wall". (I include a drawing which I believe shows the correct position of Mr Roy as he supervised pupils at that end of the hall.)

13. Likewise, I take issue with the recording of the questions and answers between Mr Fisher and me on the topic of JS forcing his way out of the classroom. Page 212. It appears as showing me saying that JS did not push Mr Roy, but only pushed past him. This is not the case. I made plain in my answers that Mr Roy was in front of the door, not at the side of it, and that JS forced his way out. Mr Roy had to follow him. I was never given a copy of the minutes of this hearing, and never saw them until the preparations for this tribunal.

14. In late September/early October 2009 I was told by Ms Fennel and Carol Gee from HR that I had to attend the appeal hearing on 6th October as a witness for the school. I was not offered any choice in the matter. I was told that this was required of me when I was called into an interview with them. Carol Gee asked me questions about the Jim ****** incident and Mr Roy's discipline. Again, I was not asked to write my own statement. What they wrote down was never shown to me or given to me, and I was never asked to sign it (or any notes) as being a true record of the interview. It was clear that Ms Fennel and Mrs Gee wanted me to concentrate on

certain aspects of events. I was asked about discipline procedures in the school and training/initiatives implemented by the faculty. I was questioned about Mr Roy's current discipline in the classroom. I think I was asked about how he controlled his classes and if he shouted a lot.

15. I have now been shown a document that I have never previously seen (page 195). I think these are the questions forming the basis of that interview with Ms Fennel and Mrs Gee in October 2009, and I think the writing in italics at the bottom is a selective summary of my answers to those questions in the interview. These same questions were then asked of me again by Mrs Gee in the appeal hearing with extras about John *******.

16. I was never given a copy of the minutes of the appeal hearing, and never saw them until the preparations for this tribunal. I have now been shown how my attendance at it was recorded (on page 277). Again, this is not an adequate account of my appearance. The HR officer Carol Gee who first questioned me is recorded as doing so, but there is no record of the questions to me from Mr Fisher.

17. It was made plain when Mr Roy was suspended that the staff were not to either discuss the matter or have any contact with him. It was therefore not until he was dismissed that I had the opportunity to discuss these events with Mr Roy. It

was only at that point that I realised it was <u>highly</u> <u>unlikely</u> that in regard to the incident in the hall with the year 7 pupil I was in fact recounting an incident with Jim ******.

18. I did not teach his year 7 class. It was only December in their first year in school, and thus I knew very few names. When Ms Fennel asked me about 'the incident in the hall with Jim ****** and Mr Roy' I recounted the incident I had seen as above – naturally presuming this was what she was referring to. I had heard and seen no other.

19. However, when finally able to discuss it with Mr Roy many months later, I recognised that what I had seen was actually the incident with the year 7 boy who had told him to "f... off" and had been ejected from the hall, NOT Jim ******. I realised this because I had noted that Mr Roy had come back into the hall afterwards without the boy and continued with his break time duty. Apparently, the incident with Jim ******, in both his and Mr Roy's accounts, had resulted in the boy being told to stay next to him, not to leave his side for the rest of break, and then his accompanying Mr Roy to the next lesson at the end of break. He had not been ejected from the hall as in the incident I had witnessed, but stayed in it. I was not asked by Ms Fennel in her investigation about two incidents in the hall that break, or shown or told what the accusation by the boy actually was, so I had no chance to realise my error.

20. If I had been asked any questions about the specific accusation made by Jim ****** I would have said in perfect truth, as I say now, that I saw no child being grabbed by his bag strap and forced through the line of waiting pupils and the welfare assistant to be held against the side wall. If that had happened I think I would have seen it because my attention would surely have been brought to it by the pupils affected by such an unusual event. If this incident had occurred as I now see is described on behalf of Jim ******, there would have been many, many witnesses, including the welfare assistant at the corner of the queue and the ladies serving food.

Uniquely, he was witness to two of the incidents, and in neither case did he see anything that he considered to be assault or inappropriate behaviour. With regards to the second incident he was the only actual witness to *anything* and his original testimony spoke of to an entirely unrelated incident. Finally, this was made clear. That those who used his testimony as grounds for my dismissal, without even noticing the incongruity, were obviously idiotic. This was yet further evidence of a whitewash.

'It would be a miracle if the decision didn't go in your favour', was Jenni's verdict. I hoped that she was correct.

Chapter Ten

Decision day

The hard bit was over. I couldn't envisage losing now but I was still nervous. The first remarkable aspect of the day's events was the fact that Fennel did not appear! Gee was there and the barrister but that was all. After all the bloody minded, pointless appearances she had made, she wouldn't be there for the denouement. What was the point? She had been humiliated every day of the tribunal, so why not now? Why not turn up for the main event? There was nothing more for her to lose now, no more ways in which her reputation could be compromised. If nothing else she could at least make a dramatic emotional outburst if the verdict was unfavourable. She might as well.

The judge began the day with his usual terse pleasantries and then read his statement. A few weeks later Jenni received a faxed copy of the judgement, excerpts from which I have included below. The first section reads like an account of the circumstances leading up to the tribunal and the second is a catalogue of reasons for deciding that I was unfairly dismissed. Naturally it is all couched in legal language, excluding phrases such as 'poisonous little gnome', 'vindictive trollop' and 'idiotic buffoon' – the sort of thing I might have included had I been called upon to write the aforementioned document. In fact, when I think about it, although phrases of this type may have been uppermost in my mind for much of the time I still resist the temptation to use them, the reason being simple paranoia. Perhaps I will live the rest of my life fearing school authorities or some other group of similarly appointed bureaucrats. Maybe I will always be looking over my shoulder, reliving every sentence I say and every action I make.

We are satisfied that an inadequate investigation was carried out by the respondent particularly having regard to the serious consequences that the claimant would face if dismissed. All the statements taken by Mrs Fennel were very short and lacking in particularity….. Moreover we are satisfied that the manner in which the matters were investigated fell outside the range of reasonable responses.

We are satisfied that it was not properly spelt out to the claimant how many allegations he was facing and the precise nature of the allegations…..

We are satisfied that it was wholly unfair, and outside the range of reasonable responses, for the first incident involving pupil A to be added as a 'count' or allegation against the claimant.

In relation to the second incident involving pupil B we do not find that the disciplinary panel or the appeal panel had reasonable grounds, having regard in particular to the inadequate investigation, for finding that the claimant had grabbed pupil B by his clothing as opposed to merely shouting at him.

In relation to the third incident involving pupil C although the disciplinary panel found that the claimant had grabbed the pupil the panel failed to make any finding as to whether the force used was significant or insignificant or as to how long the pupil had been detained for. Moreover, the panel failed to consider whether the claimant had, or might have, been acting within his legal rights pursuant to section 550A of the Education Act 1996 in detaining the pupil.

Having regard to our findings we are wholly satisfied that the decision by the disciplinary panel to dismiss the claimant fell well outside the band or range of reasonable responses.

Those are the highlights. I have read the entire eight-page document a few times now with great pleasure. It is a testament to the fact that I have come through the ordeal and been vindicated.

Before he had finished I knew I'd won my case but Jenni insisted that I try to write it all down. I just wanted to listen, to bathe in the words that made me innocent once more. After twenty months I had once again become the man I had been – officially. I was not an abuser of children, nor had I – forgive me this final indulgence – 'physically or indecently assaulted' anyone. It didn't put me back where I had been i.e. an established teacher at Collegiate High School, Blackpool but did I really want that? Did I want to re-enter the lion's den from which I had been ejected? In one sense I did. Quite apart from the need to earn money I would have liked to have gone back to just to show that I had survived, that I was innocent, that I hadn't been beaten, that I had fought back... It would have been particularly satisfying to take my place back on the school staff, even for one day, in the absence of Fennel.

There were three main points to the judgement. It was not within the remit of the judges to say that I was actually innocent, but they could do the next best thing and make my innocence an obvious facet of their deliberations. I could have won my case on a technicality – something that would have been unsatisfactory for me – but I had done much more than that. Firstly, the judges had said that I was unfairly dismissed. In other words, I should not have lost my job. Secondly, they said that had a fair procedure been followed that I would not have been dismissed. So, from a technical or legal point of view the whole affair had been a mess. Finally, they said that I had done nothing to contribute to my dismissal. None of my actions had warranted the investigation, disciplinary hearings or dismissal that followed.

I was released from the prison of other people's opinions. Not only that but the people who had put me there had found themselves in the dock and virtually convicted of wrongdoing. Their crimes ranged from malice to incompetence, via short-sightedness and stupidity. There was no official sanction but each of them was shamed nevertheless. Their punishments would be varied; Fennel had already lost her career and effectively ended her working life as a failure. For her this was just further humiliation. Wenman and Neath both 'stepped down' as governors. Whether or not this was of their volition I never found out but I suspect that someone would have had a discreet word in their ears either way.

They should never have been in positions of responsibility for which they were so ill-suited. It did seem as if the selection process for becoming a governor at Collegiate was none too rigorous – a bit like getting a commission in St John Ambulance maybe. Basically, you just had to put your name forward and then a vote took place. The paucity of volunteers for governor's positions was only matched by the paucity of active voters and through this malaise emerged the governing body. Of course,

I am biased. Some governors do a fine job... but some are idiots also.

As for Gee, Darby and Barrish I have no idea what, if anything, happened to them. Obviously, they should have been subjected to some kind of competency procedure. Clearly, they were poor at their jobs and seemingly not averse to a bit of rule bending. I felt like writing to the Director of Education asking him how his investigation into their conduct was going and volunteering my services as a witness, but I knew that their failures would be papered over in all likelihood.

And then of course there was the mysterious, felt-tip pen wielding Kate Ryding who had, without ever meeting me or hearing what I had to say, decided that I was unsuitable to work with children. What happened to her? I think I know the answer. Some people can just do what they like, say what they like, write what they like, destroy whoever's life they like. I'm not one of those people and although that means that I am usually on the receiving end, I am glad that my everyday life carries with it no obligations to attach blame unfairly. I am free to behave well.

Had I wanted revenge I was to get it in the most spectacular way imaginable.

There was the small matter of money to be argued over. An equation which included figures for loss of earnings past and in the future, minus money earned in the period following the loss of job was used to arrive at a sum. This could not exceed £66,500 and there was no means of reclaiming costs incurred. Having lost the case, the barrister naturally moved into damage limitation mode. She disputed some of the figures put together by Jenni and to have pursued the matter would have cost me more than I could ever have gained by arguing. Suffice to say that we agreed on a figure, that being £63,000.

Amusingly, having arrived at this figure and put it to her she went off with her phone to a private location to ask her boss if this was acceptable; the same sort of charade that a second-hand car salesperson uses.

'I'll just go and speak to the boss.' Why isn't the person to whom you are speaking ever actually the boss? And does he or she really have to be consulted about every fiscal undertaking?

Chapter Eleven

Spend, spend, spend

It was more money than I had ever had in my life and almost a third of Wayne Rooney's weekly wage! I could remember the time when, leaving the army, I had gone to the bank and withdrawn all my savings. It came to something like 12,000 Deutschmarks which was about £4,000 (this was in 1991). I laid the money out on my bed back in good old Block 57 and took a photograph of it. Pretty silly I know.

Of course, I didn't actually make £63,000 at all. There was no tax to pay but my fees to Jenni accounted for a third of it and I had borrowed money from Diane. I had also lost a small fortune in wages but I was fairly pleased nonetheless. That sum, paltry to a footballer, represented four years' wages (pre-tax) from St John Ambulance. It would be wrong to say that the whole ordeal had been about money but it is true to say that people for whom money is allegedly unimportant tend to have a lot of it and I had never been one of those people.

Another consideration is that the figure gives anyone who is interested a means by which to judge the extent of my former employers wrongdoing; in other words, it can be judged on a financial scale and £63,000 is a lot of anyone's money. I could have won and been given damages of £100. I hadn't quite got the maximum but I wasn't too far off it either. The barrister's quibbling cost me a few thousand but in principle I felt like I had got the full sum due to me. Had I been able to argue for hurt feelings, stress, libel, slander et cetera I might have made a million but I couldn't and I have no real complaints. Some of my workmates were shocked at how little I got and that I didn't recoup my costs but I had known what to expect from the start. It was the winning that counted not the taking part.

Of course, it was down to Jenni that I did win, although I like to think that I played my part simply by being innocent! I only understood the facts as they related to the actual events in which I was involved. What Jenni brought to proceedings was a knowledge of how the affair ought to have been conducted. She was fully conversant with the appropriate legislation (enviably more so than those who brought it to bear) and she spotted their multitude errors in a way that a lay person never could. She effectively orchestrated the tribunal; my opponents were only ever on the back foot. My innocence in itself might not have been enough to carry the day had I been relying on my own passionate but unformed defence.

Jenni laid out the facts with such clinical precision that the judges couldn't fail to understand the wrong that had been done. She took nothing for granted. I honestly think that she destroyed the case against me ten times over. The scale of her victory is actually hard to quantify in mathematical terms. In a football match, a score of 10-1 might indicate that one team had performed ten times as well as the other but the analogy fails because I don't think that our opponents actually scored that one goal. Perhaps therefore her case was infinitely better than theirs. I can't really think of anything that they said or did that planted even the tiniest seed of doubt in the judge's minds.

It was a rout, a comprehensive victory. Unequivocal.

One thing that I might legitimately have expected, but which I never received, was an apology. Graceless in defeat *and* in victory, no-one from the school or the council ever said 'sorry'. They were fairly prompt with the cheque (which of course I photographed), paying well within the three months allocated to them for that purpose, but the simple act of apologising was, it seemed, beyond them. I wasn't surprised – I held these people in contempt and that they therefore behaved contemptuously was only to be expected. They were low grade people.

I did find it amusing, however, that when I went to collect my cheque they sent it down to reception with the office junior. I personally thought that there should have been a photographer there to record the historic moment as I shook hands with the Director of Education, one of us beaming with more genuine glee than the other. Nor did I get a refund on the twenty months of my life which they effectively stole from me. From the day I was sent home to the day on which I received the judgement they had created a persona for me, one that they developed and refined and which did not flatter me in any way. Quite the reverse; I had been subjected to a deliberate attempt to destroy my good name. To portray me as a child abuser was the worst thing they could have done, the most despicable characterisation available to them.

So that was that, back to normal then? Not quite. There was still the small matter of Diane's cancer, re-establishing my career (although I was in three minds about that, at least three) and simply going back to work. The world doesn't stand still. Nor does it owe you a living. I had four days off, so we went to York to stay at my sister in law's house whilst she and her husband were in France, but after that I would be donning my green uniform and going back to work. I was happy and relieved of course but I had to work at it. I had to remind myself of what I wasn't any more (a child abuser) rather than revel in the aftermath of some great achievement. I had built up this moment so much that it was something of an anti-climax.

I am sure that it happens to everyone at some point or other; Neil Armstrong returning from the Moon, a few days leave then someone says, 'When are you coming back to work, Neil?'… Da Vinci finishing the Mona Lisa and being asked what he'd be doing next… Peter Andre writing a follow up single to 'Mysterious Girl'. I'd felt the same thing myself coming back from the Gulf War in 1991. There was no heroes' welcome, which was fair enough – I was no hero and had not actually fired a shot in anger or even whilst mildly piqued – but I still felt that my life should never be humdrum from that moment onwards.

It was the same when Diane eventually finished her cancer treatment, she could start thinking about her return to work – what a treat!

I heard from Jenni that a reporter from the Sunday Telegraph (Rebecca Lefort) wanted to write an article about me and so I made contact when I got home. She took a train from London that very day and arrived with a photographer in tow, early in the afternoon. I was astonished at the rapidity of events and to be honest I was surprised that anyone thought that my story was a big deal. It was a big deal to me obviously but then I had been rather intimately associated with the whole affair. I imagined that lots of people had found themselves in similar positions and done what I had done but something about the story grabbed attention.

Jenni was concerned that the angle to be explored was that of how teachers were treated when allegations were made against them, rather than the old chestnut of pupil indiscipline. To some extent the subsequent story reflected that but there was an element of how schools had declined and how it was the Labour party's fault. This is view that I don't strongly agree with. I prefer to take a more balanced approach and say that the Labour party is only as useless as every other party when it comes to education (and, let's face it, everything else).

We spent a few pleasant hours together before she set off with the photographer to track down Fennel and Wenman, both of whom were reluctant to talk. She particularly wanted to speak to the latter about an entry he made on Facebook on the day he took the train to Manchester to give his testimony. I have reproduced it exactly as written:

Steven Wenman on train to Manchester, got to change at preston. this will teach me not to hold the post of chair of a governing body and dismiss a teacher won't it. His third appeal, already lost his first two now at tribunal in mancherster! will he ever accept the fact?

I don't know about the wisdom of him being the chair of a governing body but I think it's clear that he might have paid more attention to his English teacher when he was a pupil. I knew nothing of this entry when he gave his evidence but it shows how shaky his grasp of the facts actually was. Quite apart from the numerous typos, it is worth saying that he didn't dismiss me – he and his fellow governors upheld the decision made by the disciplinary panel to dismiss me – quite a different matter. Nor was it my third appeal. I'd had one appeal and this was an employment tribunal. How unwise of him to make this Facebook entry but what fun I had reading it having won my tribunal. Just when I thought he couldn't appear any more foolish…

The story ran the following Sunday and I shared the front page with some fella called Cameron (Don or Derek, something like that) whose wife had had a baby. Page four was devoted entirely to me with a lovely photograph of the family, sitting beaming on the sofa. The photographer must have taken a hundred photographs, which I took to mean that we were either very photogenic or exactly the opposite. To my consternation the reporter described me as a former army officer, much in the way that someone who has served in the police would be a former police officer. The problem was that I had never been an officer. I hadn't even been an NCO! My army career, whilst varied and filled with adventures, most of which I didn't enjoy, had not seen the birth of a new military genius along the lines of Heinz Guderian or Wellington. I was more akin to Spike Milligan, but without the humour and even he became a lance-corporal! Never mind. It was a lovely article, well written and quite shocking. It gave me the opportunity to see the facts as others might see them, and the sheer unfairness of my treatment appalled me all over again.

To have won my tribunal was one thing. To have won it so comprehensively was another, but to get to tell my story to an audience so huge was simply amazing. For a short time I had become important for all the right reasons. I knew it wouldn't last. But I was wrong.

My career as an ambulance chap was drawing to a close. Diane's treatment was becoming more and more punishing; normality was a struggle. On a number of occasions, I was forced to take time off work to look after the children or take her to hospital. My employers were good about it but I became a big inconvenience to them and in October I handed in my resignation. The job had never been quite what I expected but I had been extremely grateful for it nevertheless. I stayed on as bank staff but never did a single shift and I returned my uniform exactly one year after joining. By that time my life had changed dramatically.

Chapter Twelve

Z list celebrity

After this we had another few days in York and left again on a bright Sunday morning. I wondered how my life was going to pan out from here on in. Did I go back to teaching or strike out for a new career while I was still relatively young? The latter certainly had its attractions. What would induce me to make a return to the classroom? Why would I even want to? The truth is that most of us never get to do the thing we really want to do, whether that be due to a lack of talent, drive or opportunity. Equally, I was trained to be a teacher so what else could I be?

Returning from York I realised that my phone was buzzing away in my pocket. When I finally managed to stop it became apparent that Jenni had rung me about eight times. So, outside the public toilets in Gisburn the penny dropped, so to speak: Jenni urgently needed to talk to me.

'GMTV want you. They want to interview you'. I was nonplussed. It was only a few days after winning the tribunal and someone wanted me to be on TV talking about it.

It was the start of a short burst of something like fame, something which I had not sought, expected or wanted... but having said all that, what better way to put the record straight? I am loath to use the word revenge, so I won't but I had been subjected to ordeal by deceit. Many people realised that I had lost my job, some knew why, some didn't (and presumably didn't care), others must have put two and two together, filled in the blanks with supposition... whatever. Now I could reach those people and several hundred thousand who'd never heard of me and tell them my version of events. Whether or not they actually cared that much was neither here nor there.

By the time I got home I was seriously alarmed and the scene that greeted me did nothing to calm my nerves. As I stepped out of the car I was accosted by a very tall man who claimed to be, and indeed was, a reporter. Simultaneously, a minicab turned up and the driver was looking for one David Roy. In his hand he had a telegram asking me to contact GMTV at once. I felt hounded. The reporter asked me some questions and took a photograph of me, which is the sort of thing I would expect a reporter to do.

The reporter was from the Lancashire Evening Post and his story ran a few days later. He only took one or two photos, not the hundred required by the

Sunday Telegraph but the result was fairly good, with all family members looking relaxed and content. These were the days before Diane's hair had fallen out so she was not yet wearing her wig. Her appearance would change considerably when she did start to wear it.

Next was GMTV, then in its death throes but still a popular programme. The arrangements were made for a TV crew to come to the house and an interview would be conducted from the studio. So far, so nerve-racking. They had to come early because it would be a live broadcast. Following this I was expecting a photographer from the Times Education Supplement, for they too were doing an article, and when all that was done I had to go to work!

I was walking the dog in the pitch black when a large van with the letters ITN plastered down the side passed me. Ever observant and with the reactions of a leopard I sprinted back to the house, the poor dog wondering why his exercise period was being so dramatically curtailed. I greeted the crew just as the camera man turned up and we went inside to plan my first step on the ladder to global stardom. It was heady stuff; did I want to be interviewed in the kitchen or the dining room? We settled on the dining room and the process of setting up cameras and sound equipment began. I was also filmed in the kitchen making a cup of tea and this would be used as a little teaser shot for the programme to keep people tuned in. 'Who was that making tea?', they would ask and remain transfixed until the interview started. Who wouldn't be drawn in by the spectacle of a complete stranger making a hot drink, eh?

By now the dog was upstairs and had gone back to sleep with the rest of the family. Through the little earpiece I heard the director talking to me and I talked back, although I couldn't see him. It was quite surreal. Shortly after that I heard the GMTV theme as they returned from a break and then the voice of one of the interviewers, Dan Lobb. I have no idea what he or the other presenter, Kate Garraway, asked me but I looked into the camera like a plumber looking up a pipe and dutifully answered them.

It was over in a few minutes but a second interview was needed for those people who were too lazy to get out of bed to see my first performance. We followed the same procedure; daa, da, da, da, daaaa! in the earpiece and the interview began as before… but with one slight difference. My daughter Grace had risen by this stage, made her way downstairs and put the television on. Seeing me there in glorious Technicolor was too much for her and she shouted excitedly, 'Daddy, you're on the telly!'.

Luckily, she was on the other side of the dining room door at this point. The first question was coming at me now and the camera man and I exchanged anxious looks. 'Daddy, you're on the telly!', she shouted again. I carried on like the true professional I had quickly become. Calmly, I answered the question as if this sort of thing happened to me all the time. However, Grace was not to be deterred. Even louder this time, 'Daddy you're on the telly!'. It was at this point my wife had sprinted downstairs, scooped Grace up and ushered her into the living room.

That crisis was averted but as I talked my mobile phone, which I had set on a bookshelf next to me, went off. Fortunately, it was on vibrate. When I checked it later the call had been from my old army friend, Spider. It had been no accident. We finished without incident and the crew packed up and left.

Next, I had to wait for the TES photographer to turn up. She rang in advance and asked me if I had any money. It seemed an odd question but luckily, I had, the problem being that she had left home without her purse and would need to buy petrol to get back.

When she arrived, the gargantuan task of taking the pictures began. She must have taken in excess of a hundred but it felt like thousands. I was required to sit on the sofa, with and without the family, and stand in the garden gazing thoughtfully through a forked branch of the apple tree. Then she asked me to put my uniform on. I had to anyway because I was going to work as soon as she had finished but it all felt very weird. I wasn't at all comfortable with the idea but didn't wish to rock the boat.

Again, I was photographed outside, gazing onto the distance, a man of depth and distinction, and then back inside for more of the same. The interview part had been conducted partly over the phone with help from Jenni, and the article appeared the following week. It was a full-page item with a huge photograph of me looking proud and noble in my bright green work clothes. I hated the photograph they had chosen. I thought it aged me, made me look forty-five when I wouldn't be that age for another three weeks. That done, it was off to work for another tough day, saving lives.

In the following days and weeks, there were articles in the Daily Mail, Blackpool Gazette and the prestigious Longridge Evening News. I knew that I'd hit the big time! The only one of those to which I had made a direct contribution was the Blackpool Gazette, a paper which had previously carried stories about the great successes enjoyed by the school which had sacked me. They were more than happy to change their allegiance for the sake of the story.

Next, I was contacted by a journalist from Rock FM, a local radio station. We went through the same old story in quite a low-tech way; he was equipped with nothing more than a hand-held recorder. The report was broadcast a few days later but I didn't hear it. I think that I was discussed on BBC Radio (perhaps Radio 4 and 5live) but I missed those too.

Granada reports, a local TV station, got in touch to do an interview but I was at work when they needed me. They contacted me again but I never took them up on the offer. In truth I was feeling a bit jaded. It wasn't the case that any of these people were offering me suitcases of money for my contribution to the nation's entertainment. I had a full-time job, two children and a sick wife. I wasn't complaining because the opportunity to name names and set the record straight was too good to miss but it began to be a grind.

I was summoned to Blackburn for an interview with Radio Lancashire but as I write this I don't think it has ever been broadcast. Then I was summoned to London to be interviewed for 'Lorraine', Lorraine Kelly's eponymous TV show.

Just when I thought that things had run their course and that I couldn't be surprised any more…

Chapter Thirteen

Back to the classroom

Another circumstance which hastened my departure from St John Ambulance was the offer of some teaching work in a local school. Contact had been established, through Facebook of all things, via a former colleague who had been asked by his headteacher if I wanted to work one day a week. I met the head, toured the school and started in October. It is quite unlike Collegiate. The children are not at loggerheads with the staff, there is no sense of conflict. The tension that exists in some schools is largely absent and overall the children understand that they are there to learn and that the staff are doing their best for them. It takes some getting used to. That's not to say that I don't entertain doubts. At one point it had looked unlikely that I would ever be a teacher again and throughout I seriously doubted if I even wanted to teach again, even if the opportunity arose. It is an unforgiving profession and sometimes one's place of work can seem like a nest of vipers… but isn't that just the way? Isn't every job like that?

Recently various reforms have been announced but nothing will change for the better. One ridiculous aspect of the job will be jettisoned and replaced by something different but equally silly, and so it goes on. Admit defeat, take the money, and run. It would be nice if there was no place for cynicism in a profession which is responsible for moulding our young people but it is unavoidable.

I caught the train to London, and even with a change in the Midlands reached the capital in three hours. A driver was there to meet me and hustle me across the river to the South Bank where the ITV studios are based. I met the producer in the foyer and we walked to a café around the corner where I was introduced to the soundman, the camera man and my interviewer, Craig Doyle. I was nervous but only in the same way and to the same extent as I would be when greeting any new people. I was unsure what they wanted me to say or what they expected me to be like but took some reassurance from the knowledge that my previous TV appearance must have been sufficiently good for them to ask me back; it was either that or they were desperate beyond belief.

We had a coffee and my new media buddies chatted to me. At this point I still had an irrational worry that people were trying to catch me out. I was of course beyond that now but couldn't quite shake my distrust of people. As we chatted about the state of schools, the camera man said quite innocently to me, 'you must feel like smacking them sometimes'. I was at once on my guard. 'No', I said unconvincingly. My apparent alarm caused some amusement.

'We're not here to catch you out, you can relax', someone said and I realised that it was true. The basis of the story was the unfairness of my treatment and the problems facing teachers in British schools. It was categorically *not* a last-ditch attempt to catch me out or give me a rope to hang myself.

Craig Doyle ran through the questions and I ran through my answers and then we changed location to another café overlooking the Thames. I had forgotten just how grand the city was. I decided that I would return someday and in fact I was summoned back the following week! Filming would take place upstairs and as the crew set up, Craig and I chatted again, talking about our shared 'Irishness', his from the South and mine from the North. The producer stood guard by the door as things got underway lest someone stray into our interview on their way to the toilet. Naturally, this happened a few times and I noticed some very startled looks as people clocked the camera, the lights and the sound equipment as they tried to nip unobtrusively to the loo. We also had to stop as the hand dryer went off. I wasn't yet a prima donna who got upset by such interruptions to my starry media career but the time would come for sure. When I returned the following week, I demanded rose petals be scattered everywhere I went.

Craig and I sat opposite each other at a small table, with the camera some distance behind his left shoulder, pointing at me. He asked his questions, fifteen of them, and I answered in what I hoped was a sensible, concise, tactful manner.

'So how did you feel when you discovered that these accusations had been made?'

'So, tell me exactly what happened.'

'Don't you feel angry about the treatment you received?'

I can't remember my answers and to be honest I can't remember if those were even amongst the questions, but they are representative of *the sort of thing* I was asked. The camera cut a few times as I stumbled over my words and on fewer occasions as he stumbled over his, but it wasn't live so it didn't matter. When all the questions had been asked the camera moved so that it was now behind me looking at Craig Doyle. He attempted to ask me the questions again, although he couldn't quite remember them all and I had to sit and nod or look like I was talking. What I was not required to do was answer the questions again, so I just looked at him blankly as he asked me the questions. It felt very like bad manners and was quite disconcerting. From this strange assembly of footage an interview was constructed, although only about three of the questions/responses were shown. There was a lot of editing and I only ever saw the interview in brief the following week just before my next TV experience.

Shortly after that we parted company and I made my way on foot back to the station, stopping off for a celebrity tea at the famous, small Scottish restaurant. As my chicken nuggets arrived I was able to ponder the world of celebrity and what TV stars ate. Was this it? It wasn't all glamour, or in my case none of it was. I looked around at my fellow feedees and couldn't spot any other stars. No Terry Wogan or Tess Daly. No Winona Ryder or Beau Bridges. Not even Dale Winton. Maybe this was the wrong McDonalds.

I counted my chicken nuggets to see if they had discreetly slipped an extra one into the box as a courtesy for patronising their establishment – a sort of payment in kind for the free publicity – but there were only six. Not one person asked me for my autograph. No one rushed up to me and said breathlessly, 'Are you David Roy?' It wasn't just because the interview hadn't been shown – I was a fully-fledged TV veteran by this point. Maybe in time I would come to enjoy my continued anonymity. How often do we hear the stars lament their lack of privacy? No such worries for me.

A week later I was back, this time for a live TV appearance in the studio. The producer or researcher who rang had actually wanted the whole family there, but Diane was concerned that she wouldn't be up to it and so I went by myself, catching the train on Sunday and being met by a car yet again. This time it was a BMW and I confessed to the driver that it was the nicest car I'd ever been in, at which he laughed. He dropped me off at the City Inn near the studios and I checked in like the hardened globe-trotting celebrity that I was. It was the sort of place that immediately made me feel unworthy, like a Beverley Hills Hill Billie. I'd spent a good part of my life 'roughing it' to a greater or lesser degree.

Polite, attentive staff worried me, as if contact with them left me open to an endless succession of faux pas. I was well-mannered in an Ulster Protestant way; undemonstrative, reticent, ill at ease, constantly feeling slightly inferior to those around me. I worried about causing offence, not leaving a tip or a tip which was too small, too big, using the wrong fork to eat my soup… Even the lifts conspired against me. Whatever floor I was on wasn't listed next to any of the lifts and eventually I just stepped into the next one that descended. Not only did I feel like a bumpkin but I thought that everyone else could tell that I was just by looking at me.

My room was very swish and the restaurant even more so. I dined alone, conscious of the fact that I had been allocated a certain sum to pay for my food and wanting to make sure that I didn't go over. It wasn't paying the difference that bothered me but the embarrassment factor. I had a glass of water, chose a middling sized steak for my main meal and a nice but relatively modest pudding. It still came to more than the amount I had to spend! Having finished and let my food settle I strode confidently from the restaurant only to be pursued by a foreign waiter who needed to know which room I was in for the purposes of billing. My first *faux pas*.

Despite my apprehension I slept well but was up early for my journey to the studio, skipping breakfast as if I didn't deserve it. My car was waiting but I had been downgraded to a Toyota Prius. Presumably the hotel had rung ahead and said that I was an idiot who didn't understand the procedure for eating in a posh restaurant and not to waste too prestigious a car on me. Minutes later the car dropped me off at the TV superstar entrance and I found myself in the studio foyer, a surprisingly tatty place furnished with one plastic chair of the type used in school dinner halls (ironically).

Behind me came one of my fellow guests, Jo Wood, wife or former wife of Rolling Stone, Ronnie

Wood. Gallantly I offered her my plastic chair and with equal gallantry she refused. I didn't blame her; it looked pretty manky even without me sitting in it. From then on, I was in the care of various producers and assistants, all of whom introduced themselves and all of whose names I immediately forgot with an alacrity that I never seem to possess for any other purpose, like returning a library book or buttoning a coat.

I was taken to make-up and spray painted to make me look less like a weary corpse. Then I was shown the interview I had done with Craig Doyle, or what was left of it. It was the closest I ever came to seeing one of my TV appearances. An interview with my arch rival, Michael Gove, the Secretary of State for Education, was to be shown also and it was upon this that I had to comment.

I was led down to the studio and watched Celia Walden and Andrew Pierce give their withering round up of the top newspaper stories for that day, laying the boot into Wayne Rooney in particular who was undergoing a spat with his employers Manchester United. It was something to do with money; £200,000 a week? It was a slightly surreal experience to stand in the gloom and watch the piece, invisible and as yet irrelevant. It was almost like an out of body experience.

Once again, my interviewer was Kate Garraway and when during a commercial break I was plonked on the sofa next to her she said that she remembered talking to me before, which made me feel like slightly less of a nonentity than I was in reality. I was introduced and then we watched the two video clips before I was asked about the government's new proposals for education.

I had been given a bit of clue about these and had decided that my response to one of the new ideas, a thrust to put greater evidence on literacy to improve behaviour – would be something like, 'if you can't get the children to behave in the first place then how can you improve their literacy?'. I thought then, and I still do, that it was a valid point but the problem was that once I was required to respond I couldn't remember if he had actually said it in the clip they had shown and so my witty riposte withered like a vine in the sun. As for the rest of it, I waffled on about parental responsibility and how the rot had set in (in terms of children's behaviour in schools) many years ago. I told them that I wondered if it was too little, too late. At least I think I did. I must have performed adequately because there was more stardom to come but at the time I really didn't know if anything I said sounded reasonable or sensible.

I worried slightly about my accent, a once impenetrable Ulster Scots 'brogue', I suppose you might call it, but I think I was understood because Kate Garraway did not look blankly at me when I spoke. It had not always been so. On my first trip to the mainland with people from other parts of the country I realised that my accent posed problems for them. Living in Northern Ireland with other Northern Irish people simply never alerted me to this possibility. I remember once saying to my mum that I didn't think I really had an accent and she looked at me as if I was mad.

It was over in no time at all. By that I don't mean that the time flew by, although it did. I mean it literally took a very short time to conduct the interview. Perhaps when I had thought I was waffling I was in reality being rather terse… but I have never seen the interview, so I don't know. Actually, being there is no substitute for watching!

As Kate Garraway gave details of a competition, I was led away from the sofa again and whisked off, pausing briefly for Jo Wood to tell me how well I had done. I took that as a good sign; a bona fide celebrity thought I had done okay or was that my reward for having offered her the one and only ITV celebrity chair earlier on? I had been told that the next stop would be to have my make-up removed but it never happened for some reason and my car was waiting, so without much further ado I sped off to the station again. A few onlookers peered into the car as we drove out hoping to see someone famous but by the look on their faces I just didn't cut the mustard in that respect. I felt like apologising to them. What a disappointment I must have been. Not so much a has-been but a 'never-was'. When I checked my phone, which I had left behind in the green room during my interview, I discovered that Spider had rung me again, the bugger.

The train was bound for Edinburgh, stopping off at Preston and assorted outposts on the way. You can imagine that as a famous TV personality I was rather disappointed to find that I didn't have a seat. I spent the entire journey slumped next to an out of order lavatory talking to a doctor from Portugal and an illegal immigrant from Africa. I began to feel really ill after a short time. I had all the disadvantages one might associate with feeling ill on a high-speed train, stranded next to the toilet, without even the singular advantage of having somewhere private to throw up. The journey was a torment. I was so squashed in that had I actually been sick I would have spattered half a dozen people as well as myself. Maybe it was post televisual stress disorder (PTSD) or the rank coffee I bought in the station at the time when I believed I would be sitting down on my journey home (I was just behind Clare Balding in the queue).

It was a slightly pathetic and low-key end to my TV odyssey. Not only that but I was still wearing my make-up of course, which I personally found rather discomfiting. It's okay if you're Boy George or someone but frankly I'm not him and never have been. Upon my return Diane insisted we all go to

Pizza Hut which, with my stomach still churning, was high on my list of places to avoid.

My brush with celebrity was nearing its end but there were a couple of adventures in broadcasting left. A phone call from Daybreak, successor to GMTV, confirmed that there was life in the old story yet. This was prompted by the Education Secretary's latest pronouncement. I didn't know what it was but felt confident that I could answer questions about it. By now, however I was thoroughly weary and so when they asked if they could come to the house for a live interview I declined. I had a couple of weeks work at my new school and simply couldn't be bothered and said so. Daybreak was suffering from poor ratings and obviously I, media darling and education superstar, was being drafted in to give things a boost, but even so…

With obvious disappointment the producer admitted defeat and the matter was closed for about two minutes until she rang back.

'We really want you on the show', she explained. 'We could come to the school and interview or interview you outside…'

'I don't think so because obviously the school know nothing about it', I explained. I pictured the rest of the staff turning up at work and seeing a supply teacher being interviewed in front of a TV camera – it wasn't the sort of impression I wanted to make at all.

'Okay we can come to your house, set up outside, get everything ready and then the crew can text you when they want you. All you'd have to do would be go outside give the interview and then you could go back in. It would only take a couple of minutes'. They sounded desperate. 'We can even pay you if you want', she added. I thought that was an odd thing to say. How was I supposed to respond? *No thanks I am doing it for the benefit of humanity. To accept payment would be to cheapen the whole experience'.*

Let's face it, if they wanted to pay that was fine; they wanted me, not the other way around. I was bathing the children, when about ten minutes later she rang for a third time. My wife answered this time and once again there had been a change of plan. It would be too dark to film outside so the crew would have to come inside like last time. In my absence Diane agreed to the new plan.

The same camera man turned up the following day along with two other blokes I hadn't met before. There was to be only one interview and this time I wasn't filmed making a cup of tea, that practice having been banned, due to its lack of entertainment value. Once again, I was interviewed by Kate Garraway. It was my third different show but the same presenter each time. I wasn't complaining though, she seemed very nice. By now I knew her better than some of my relatives.

Finally, my fame caught up with me.

'Were you on the telly this morning, sir?', asked a year seven boy.

'I was indeed', I answered modestly. By the time I saw him again he had told the entire class about my fame and I had to explain briefly why I had come to be on their screens. After that it settled down. Nothing was ever mentioned again.

After Christmas I was once again asked to appear on an ITV morning show. This time money was mentioned in a slightly less vague way but I needn't have worried. Having begun packing my bags for the trip down to London they rang back and said they didn't need me after all. Michael Gove had agreed to come into the studio and so I was dropped.

I never did get paid.

Another government proposal that has been put forward is to employ ex-service personnel as teachers to help bring discipline back into schools. I would dearly love to be invited back to talk about that one. I can testify to the fact that having been in the forces does absolutely nothing for you when you become a teacher. I am sure that in their attempts to discredit me, the school authorities must have examined the old 'psychologically damaged combat veteran' angle. Martin Fisher certainly suspected that they might. It's a laughable idea, but one given enormous credence through the medium of American war films. That millions of people made it through two world wars and went on to live normal lives doesn't seem to come into it. Every soldier, sailor and airman, no matter how slight their brush with combat, is now very likely to be considered a closet lunatic with psychotic tendencies, and liable to wield a gun for very unsporting purposes at the slightest provocation. No wonder then, that a man who had served in the first Gulf War, driving a Land Rover, talking on a radio, digging trenches and cleaning dixies, could so easily be tipped over the edge into acts of violence against children. I probably had thousand-yard stare and trench foot too.

No, involving ex-servicemen and women in teaching is just a stupid gimmick. They would only have to endure the same things as every other teacher, the only difference being that it would be even more galling for them. They would have no recourse to military discipline, that being a genuine deterrent admittedly. What could they do to a naughty child that any other teacher couldn't do? Charge them and get them fourteen days detention in the guardroom? Send them for a ten-mile run in full kit? Bury them up to their necks in sand, pour honey on their head, and leave them to the desert animals?

Chapter Fourteen

The Future

So, I never did become a TV superstar with my own current affairs programme and an entourage whose sole job it is to throw rose petals in my path and make sure that my bottled Perrier water is at exactly the right temperature... but I have no complaints, not really. It was important that justice was done and it was, so that's fine. The people who tried to bring about my downfall perhaps only hastened theirs. The turnaround in my fortunes still astonishes me, however. My job, my career and my good name were taken from me. I was reported to the Child Protection Agency (at least I think I was but I never heard from them) and for many months I couldn't get even the humblest of jobs. From there to winning the tribunal in fine style with the strongest possible judgement in my favour and then to the round of interviews for the papers and radio and finally my three appearances on television... I used my fifteen minutes of fame well.

It was Jenni Watson who gave me hope and brought me back from the deepest pits of ignominy. My family and a select group of friends stood by me and many others let me down. I heard that one of the officials in the Local Education Authority was rather pleased at my victory and that I took on the establishment and fought back but I never heard from him personally or in my hour of need.

I never did get my apology of course but in a way I am glad; it proves that my opinion of the people with whom I was dealing was correct all along.

So, was I happy? Well yes and no, but within a few weeks of winning the tribunal I realised that all was not as it should be. I felt down most of the time. I spent some of my money but derived little satisfaction from doing so. The holidays I had promised the family didn't happen because of Diane's treatment and everything felt a bit flat. I supposed that it would take time to adjust but I never did. Eventually, I returned to the GP's surgery and was prescribed the tablets I had been on previously to treat depression. I hadn't felt the need for them before – if I found myself depressed it was easy to pinpoint the reason. Not only that but I feared that using them was only going to be taken as a sign of my inherent mental fragility.

But now I am free to view the rest of my life through Prozac tinted glasses. It's a sort of compromise happiness but better than some of the alternatives. I often count my blessings as I have done for a good many years now, and most of the time that serves to lift me out of my shallow puddle of despondency. Generally, I am free to worry about all the stupid inconsequential things I used to worry about and, although I am not sure if that's a good thing or a bad thing, it is probably indicative of a return to the brittle tissue of happiness with which we are humanly blessed.

Throughout it all, the world still turned and I didn't really matter much in the great global scheme. Lots of people suffered injustices equal to mine and often with more profound effects. Some of those people fought back and prevailed, some fought back and lost, some never fought back at all, either through a lack of will or a lack of opportunity. I didn't spend months or years rotting in a prison cell but I felt imprisoned nevertheless, branded with a stigma that acted like a visible badge of shame. The truth is that some people must still believe that I was guilty of something. That is not to say that Ms Gillian Wendy Fennel, former Headteacher of Collegiate High School is among them.

Postscript

Recently, I went for a meal with the battered remnants of the science department in which I had worked for so many years. They were operating under a new regime, for the school was about to 'turn a corner' and a new dawn would soon be upon them. One of the teachers I spoke to had just been suspended as an investigation was conducted into his behaviour, which sounded familiar. Another had just resigned following a competency procedure in which he got the distinct impression that he was expected to leave. Another had just finished the 'support' package given to him to help him through a competency procedure and yet another was still undergoing a similar procedure. Another teacher who had only been at the school for two terms and who previously been judged to have been an outstanding teacher, was undergoing both a disciplinary procedure and a competency procedure!

In total twenty-one teachers have come under some sort of investigation in a period of less than a year – a statistic which says much more about the local authority and the school's managers than it does about the unfortunate individuals involved.

My useless union representative had left. It seemed as if only one teacher in that department was not under the cosh and only because he was an obsequious toady who just happened to be on the board of governors. That last fact can only be a coincidence, of course.

Am I glad that I left? Well, in the course of writing this book I think that I have used up my allocation of clichés, so I'll leave you to decide.

Second postscript

It is now more than two years after my tribunal victory. Collegiate High School is on the verge of being merged with another school. This is happening because the school roll has diminished by two thirds! We are supposed to believe that this is because of a falling birth rate. Is the birth rate really only one third of 1998 levels?

The merger will involve knocking down Collegiate's perfectly good buildings, building a new school on the same site, filling it with the same children and continuing to let the British education system and British society in general go to hell in a handcart. That's progress for you. Fennel is now an OFSTED advisor, telling teachers how to teach and headteachers how to run schools. Meanwhile, I am still struggling to get work. At present, I am employed as a welfare assistant in my daughters' school, earning about thirty pounds a week. I would get twice as much on the dole.

My wife has been in remission from her cancer for two years, so every day is a blessing.

I regularly apply for jobs with Lancashire County Council. To date I have not had so much as an acknowledgment that my applications have even been received. I have applied for countless jobs in the last two years, had three interviews and been turned down in each case. I will keep trying.

Third Postscript

Can you have a third postscript? It is now a few years down the line. The children are growing up quickly and can barely remember those dark events or the media interest that ensued. I now work in a little school in the neighbouring county and spend the week away from home living in a caravan, simply because I have been unable to get a job closer to my house. It is not ideal but a job is a job and this one is better than most.

Collegiate has fared less well insofar as it has been pulled down and replaced with a new school. The school buildings, of course, were not the problem; it was the management that needed to be pulled down and replaced with some sort of competent body.

Bluffers rule.